# THE BEST OF JOHN HARTLEY

*An account of his life &*
*"The Clock Almanack"*

# THE BEST OF JOHN HARTLEY

## An account of his life &
## "The Clock Almanack"

JOHN WADDINGTON-FEATHER

WALTERSGILL

Published in 2007 by
Waltersgill
Photography & Publishing,
17 Wrenbeck Drive, Otley,
West Yorkshire, LS21 2BP

ISBN 978 0 9556454 0 2




Designed By
Waltersgill

Printed and bound by
Smith Settle, Gateway Drive,
Yeadon, Leeds, LS19 7XY

# Acknowledgements

The author wishes to thank the following people for the great help he has received in compiling this account of the life and work of John Hartley:

*The editors and members of*
*The Yorkshire Dialect Society.*

*Dr. Ian Dewhirst, former Reference Librarian,*
*Keighley Public Library.*

*Mr. T. E. Winpenny, "Halifax Courier Ltd.".*

*Mr. Anthony Grey, journalist and writer.*

*Mrs. F. M. Thorley, Thorne, near Doncaster.*

*Mrs. Dorothy Pruitt, Pennsylvania, U. S. A.*
*(Great-granddaughter of John Hartley).*

*Mr. Bob Duckett, former Reference Librarian*
*at Bradford Central Library, for re-discovering*
*and preserving the manuscript of this book.*

*Special Collections, J.B. Priestley Library,*
*University of Bradford.*

*Dedicated to*
*The Yorkshire Dialect Society*

# Contents

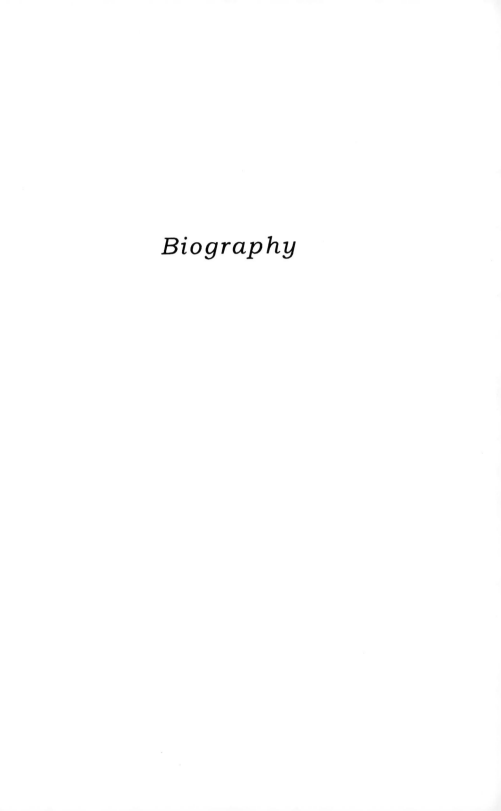

*Biography*

# Biography

The tremendous vitality of nineteenth century Yorkshire is reflected nowhere more strongly than in the dialect writings of John Hartley. He attempted all three styles of writing — poetry, drama and prose; and though much of his verse is doggerel, some of it reaches real excellence. Most of his poems, like "Bite Bigger", were very popular in his day and are still widely read; but all of his writing shares one feature, which still interests us. It catches in no uncertain manner, and in detail, the social conditions and attitudes of Victorian urban Yorkshire, a new industrial society which had grown in the few decades before Hartley's birth and which during his lifetime was to explode further. Some idea of the phenomenal population growth may be gained, when it is realised that in the year of Hartley's birth (1839), the West Riding had just over one million people living there, but when he died in 1915 there were well over three million.

John Hartley's real strength lay in his superb command of dialect in the essay and short story. He was also an early editor of a literary form peculiar to the working-class writers of Yorkshire in the 19th century — the dialect almanac. The history of Yorkshire dialect almanacs can be read in B. T. Dyson's article in the Yorkshire Dialect Society's "Transactions" for 1975. Suffice it to say here that they were written for, and very often by, urban workers, a new British social class in the rapidly expanding towns and cities of South and West Yorkshire. Hartley took over the editorship of the "Halifax Original Illuminated Clock Almanack" in 1866 and continued editing it till his death. At the peak of its success it sold 80,000 copies annually, and it continued to be published in dialect by a variety of editors (and contributed to by Yorkshire writers of the calibre of J. B. Priestley) right down to 1957, when Watmoughs of Idle, near Bradford, published the last edition.

John Hartley was born on October 19th, 1839, at 7 Bedford Street, Halifax. His father was a tea merchant and draper, and his mother was a staunch Quaker. John Hartley received some formal schooling before he was an apprenticed to James Ackroyd & Sons as a designer in worsted tapestries at the age of twelve. He worked there for over twenty years till he set sail for America in 1872.

Dialect-writing among the Yorkshire urban classes was already well established when Hartley was a boy. Indeed, Yorkshire dialect had flourished as a literary medium since the seventh century and throughout the middle ages; but it developed strongly among the new workers swelling the towns. Hartley was particularly influenced by a Lancashire dialect-writer, Edwin Waugh, whose East Lancashire dialect was very much akin to Hartley's West Yorkshire dialect and whose works were popular on both sides of the Pennines.

As a young man, Hartley joined one of the literary clubs which were fashionable at that time among working men; often the clubs were a by-product of the Mechanics' Institutes where many workers received their only schooling (It was at the Bradford Mechanics' Institute that Professor Joseph Wright of Oxford University first received any education in depth, while he was still a worker at Salt's Mill. Wright later compiled the first English Dialect Dictionary and was a contemporary of Hartley.) The literary club Hartley was a member of was called the Beacon Club and it met in a pub, the Corporation Arms, for its weekly meetings. It was there he recited the first poem he wrote, "Bite Bigger", which still remains a great favourite despite its tear-jerking sentiment. More important, it does record a real situation of the time, the appalling poverty in Victorian Yorkshire, which drove pauper children to eating gutter garbage. The poem was an immediate success and like many dialect poems of the day, it sold hundreds of copies at a penny a time. This cheap broadsheet method of selling verse was common among Yorkshire dialect writers, as it had been among the ballad-sellers of London.

"Bite Bigger" in every way launched John Hartley on his dialect-writing career. It put him in front ranks of Yorkshire dialect poets and it brought him to the notice of the son of Alfred Wilson, an auctioneer and hatter in Halifax, who had established an almanac in 1865, primarily as an advertising journal. He had called this almanac "The Original Illuminated Clock Almanack" because his hat-shop in Corn Market had an illuminated clock over it, which was well known for miles around. That edition for 1865 was edited by a dancing teacher called James Bland, but Wilson's son was so impressed by young Hartley's poetry that he offered John Hartley the editorship in 1866 and also financed the new magazine, which retained its original title until it became known as "John Hartley's Original Clock Almanack" in 1877. Hartley's first edition came out in October 1866 and was issued in two forms, a paperback edition, which sold at 2d a copy, and a hardback edition selling at 1s. The paperback number remained the most popular and sold 5,000 copies in a few weeks (Hartley must have been the first regional writer to move from paperback to hardback books as his popularity grew; quite the reverse of what happens to popular writers now).

A great deal about John Hartley's earlier life remains a mystery. For example, it is not clear when exactly he married for the first time, but it must have been some time in 1863 or 1864. Little, too, is known about the first marriage. If the dialect stories involving his wife up to the 1880's are anything to go by (and he certainly based the fictional character Mally on his second wife after their marriage in 1880, which was a happy marriage) his first marriage may have been rather tempestuous. Certain it is that in 1872 he suddenly left home and sailed for America, an America still in a state of flux a few years after the Civil War. To us this may seem very erratic, but it was a relatively common practice in the 19th century textile trade for men to cut loose and leave work and home for days, even weeks, together and go off on heavy drinking sprees, known in dialect as "goin' on t'rant". Male weavers and wool-combers were especially notorious for this and would turn up at work after their rant out just as if nothing had happened.

In his book, "Grimes's Trip to America", published in 1877, two years after he returned, Hartley recaptures some of his experiences in North America in a series of letters, all written as dialect anecdotes under the pseudonym of Sammywell Grimes — a loveable character he developed further during his writing career, who partners an equally lovable, if sharp-tongued, wife, Mally. In the first letter, Hartley may give us a clue to his sudden exit from Bradford, where he was living, for America. Things had not been going too good for Sammywell at work and after a row with his boss he is given the sack. He returns home expecting some sympathy from his wife, but instead receives only shrewish comments about his lack of common sense and his wanderlust, which unsettles him periodically (Sammywell had earlier been to London on an impulsive jaunt).

The following extract captures his mood:

"..... Shoo lewkt at me as faal as a mewl an' sed, 'It's just what aw expected, for ther's nivver been noa livin' wi' thi sin tha coom thro Lundun, an' my belief is, if tha had ony sense when tha went, tha lost it afore tha come back.'

'Well, 'aw says, 'aw dooant knaw 'at aw'm altered mich, but tha sees aw've leearned summat wi' goin away.'

'Tha's gain'd a lot o'knowledge reight eniff,' shoo sed, 'but if all tha knaws wer i't' "Yorksher Pooast" an' all tha doesn't wer i't' "Bradford Observer" aw've a gooid idea which 'ud be t'biggest paper.'

'Nivver heed,' aw sed, 'just give us a bit o' cheese an' breead an' a drop o' hooam brewed.'

'Tha'll get noa breead an' cheese here, nor hooam brew'd nawther,' shoo sed, 'it's time enuff to tawk abaat eytin' an' drinkin' when tha's been workin', an' tha willn't hev awther bite or sup i' this haase wol tha's gooan an' begged on ageen, or else getten another shop.'

'Well,' aw thowt, 'this is comin' it rayther too strong.' Soa aw says, 'If tha doesn't gi' me some cheese an' breead aw'l goa whear aw can get some, if aw have to goa to America for it, as sewer as my name's Sammywell.'

'Ay, aw wish tha wod,' shoo sed,' it'll be t'happiest day o' my life when aw know thar't gooin' across t'salt seah: but tha hesn't pluck enuff for that.'" Already irate with the treatment he has received from his employers that day, this taunt from his wife is the final straw. He stamps out of the house, taking his bankbook with him to draw out some money to go on the razzle. When he's had enough to drink, Mally's sarcastic words, that he hadn't pluck to go to America, come back to him; so without more ado Sammywell buys a ticket to Liverpool, and there he sets off for America. His subsequent letters to his friend in England, John Jones Smith, describe the voyage across the Atlantic (No pleasant experience in those days for a steerage passenger and vividly described by Hartley.). They also describe what conditions were like in North America for the new immigrant. There are some poignant cameos of life in Quebec and Montreal, where his ship docked, and where he graphically describes an ice-breaking trip up the St. Lawrence, which is recounted later in this book.

Later, Hartley moved down to New York and Washington, from which city he signs his letter "Colonel Grimes – as ivvery other chap ye meet is awther a colonel or a general, an' aw think aw may as well be i't' fashion." His trip took him to Detroit, East Saginaw, Michigan, and then to Syracuse, before he arrived in Philadelphia where he decided to return to England.

His final letter has all the essence of Hartley's humour – dry, pawky, sardonic and sentimental; above all, it is humour exquisitely timed, as shown in this episode where he describes his return home after three years abroad. I begin the narrative where he is describing leaving the train at Bradford railway station:

"T'same pooarters wor wheelin' t'same trucks, t'same owd bills wor stuck up i't' same owdplaces; one or two chaps nodded at me just t'same as if they'd seen mi t'day befoor, an' after puttin' mi box i't' left luggage office aw started for hooam. T'Taan Hall wor chimin' t'same owd tunes, t'same muck seemed to be i't'gutters, an' t' same ponds o' watter

14

i't'streets. Aw'd been varry anxious to get hooam, but as aw gate nearer aw began to slacken mi speed, for aw didn't feel varry sewer whether aw should be made welcome or not. Just as aw'd getten to t'yard end who should aw see but ahr Hebsibah stood aght side nursin' a little babby, an' as sooin as shoo saw me shoo held it up an' sed, "Lewk at thi grondad, doy!" That wor all 'at wor wanted to put aght t'last spark o' youthful frolic 'at wor left. Aw'd oft wondered what they'd mak on mi when aw gate back, an' monny a scoor o' times had aw wondered what they wor doin' when aw wor away; but aw'd nivver thowt 'at they'd mak a grondfayther on me.

"Why, tha doesn't mean to tell me 'at tha's getten wed, does ta?"

"For sewer aw have, an' ahr Ezra too; an' if ye'd stopt away mich longer mi mother'd ha' been lewkin aght for a fresh un."

Aw went inside, an' thear wor Mally, lewkin' owder an' moor careworn nor when aw left her, but t'same Mally still. Aw tried to say summat, but a little bit o' phlegm stuck at top o' mi throit, an' aw could get nowt aght. Shoo picked up t'pooaker wi' one hand an' began to scale t'fire, an' wi't other shoo kept wipin' her nooas wi' her apron, as if shood getten a varry bad cowd; an' mi een wattered a gooid bit. Hebsibah ran aght to tell t'neighbours 'at aw'd come back, an' when we wor bi us sen Mally turned raand an' sed, "It's ta'en thi a long time to get that cheese an' breead an' drop o' homebrewed."'

During John Hartley's absence from England, the "Clock Almanack" was edited by other well-known Yorkshire dialect writers, Bradfordian Edmund Hatton, in 1873 and 1874, and by the Shipley born James Burnley in 1875 and 1876. In 1877, Hartley once again took over the editorship, and in the number for that year the clock face, instead of numbers, is lettered "John Hartley"; not "Wilson Hatter" as it had been previously. It remained in that format until the almanac went defunct.

When he returned to England in 1875, Hartley moved to London for a while, earning his living by his pen and giving recitals of verse both in dialect and in Standard English. He lived this literary sort of life for five years in London, during which time he wrote prolifically. Before he left for America (where he had hoped to make his living as writer, too) Hartley had published "Hartley's Yorkshire Budget" – a book that contained the whole of Rambling Remarks from the "Clock Almanacks" of 1867 to 1871. This was followed by "Yorkshire Ditties" (first and second series), "Yorkshire Tales", "Yorksher Puddin" (1876), "Seets i'Lundun" (1876), "Grimes' Trip to America" (1877), and "Seets i'Paris" (1878) – the last-named containing an exquisite description of a trip to the top of the Eiffel Tower. Hartley also tried his hand at writing popular novelettes in Standard English; melodramatic works such as "A Rolling Stone – a tale of wrongs and revenge", as well as dialogues for popular recitals, like "The Sprit Rapper – a humorous dialogue for seven male characters", which came from his pen by the dozen. But his efforts in "Classic English", as these works are described, nowhere near match his writings in dialect. It is in dialect that his best descriptive narratives are to be found, recording all manner of experiences in all manner of places; for, unlike most dialect-writers, he was a much travelled man for his day and, like Dickens, whom he resembled to a surprising degree, his keen sense of observation and human sympathy captured a wealth of detail that escaped better educated but less understanding men.

In 1880, Hartley moved north again and added the occupation of licensee to the many jobs he had had since leaving the mill at Halifax eight years earlier. He became "Mine host" at the Druid Arms in Bradford, but he left there to live in Leeds the following year. Here, too, his stay was brief and reflected the near frenetic changes of mind and inclination he manifested in his forties, for he quit Leeds in January 1882, to travel to America again; this time with his second wife and the sons of his first marriage. One of his sons became a Baptist Minister, the Revd. Dr. John Hartley, and stayed behind in the States when Hartley and the rest of the family returned to England twelve years later and another became involved in the trades union movement in the States. Descendents of John Hartley still live there today. What is remarkable in this period is that he continued editing the "Clock Almanack" throughout his twelve-year stay in Philadelphia, where he set up business in carpets and upholstery.

His second wife was Sophia Ann Wilson, the only daughter of Wilson, the hatter, who had founded the "Clock Almanack". Whatever his first marriage was like, there is no doubt his second marriage was a very happy one, and Hartley's later Mally is based on the personality of Sophia Wilson. She was a tolerant – one might say long-suffering woman with similar tastes and outlook to Hartley and this was fortunate for him, because he was constantly on the move after their return to England in 1894 following a bank crash in America which ruined them.

In 1895, he was living in Harehills Terrace, Leeds, and the following year at Shadwell. Two years later, they sold up their home and went to stay in Blackpool for a few months, leaving behind a daughter who taught at Roundhay Road Board School. From Blackpool they moved finally to Liscard in Cheshire, where he died in 1915. Writing was his main source of livelihood during this period and he wrote for another firm of publishers, W. Nicholson & Sons of London and Wakefield as well as Watmoughs of Idle. Nicholson's brought his works before a much wider range of public including a growing international public. Yet for Hartley life was always a financial struggle. He could not manage money and it was his wife's sense of economy and able management, which pulled them through some bad patches (She was an accomplished musician and gave lessons to eke out their income.).

In 1909, an unsuccessful attempt was made to obtain a Civil List Pension for him, such as had been given to the Dorset dialect poet, William Barnes. Hartley was disappointed, yet he shrugged it off, for he was rarely an unhappy man and his writings reflect his optimism again and again despite the setbacks life gave him. It was this unfailing optimism, which endeared him to his public, for he shared with them the many knocks life hands out; and he frequently expressed the experiences and the philosophies of life, which were the lot of the West Riding worker. On his 70th birthday in 1909, a banquet in his honour was held at the Great Northern Hotel, Bradford. On that occasion he was presented with a life-size portrait and a purse containing 100 guineas, no inconsiderable sum in those days, which reflected the deep affection and esteem of his fellow Yorkshire men and women. Nor was this the last tribute paid him. In 1912 another public tribute was made when a banquet was held for him at the Old Clock Hotel, Halifax, to celebrate his 73rd birthday. He was given a purse of £74 and an album containing the names of all guests, one of whom, Mrs. A. B. Wakefield of Hipperholme, who made the presentation, hoped their gift "would bring him consolation when he was reading to his Mally by his fireside in the peaceful and restful days of life."

However, both John Hartley and his wife by this time were suffering ill health and he was virtually housebound much of his later years by a crippling illness in his legs. Mentally, though, he was as alert as ever and continued editing the "Clock" right up to his death, the year of its fiftieth issue. Visitors in his later years in Cheshire found him as "Yorkshire" as ever, always keen to discuss the works of his contemporary dialect-writers such as Ben Preston, whom in earlier years he used to visit at Bingley, and the Lancashire writer, Edwin Waugh, who influenced Hartley's first writings greatly.

On January 22nd 1915, Mrs. Hartley died, but in September of the same year, John Hartley sought the companionship of another wife, Mrs. Annie Spencer, a Mancunian and retired schoolmistress, who, like him, was widely travelled and a writer. Their marriage was short-lived, however, for John did not long survive "Mally". Three months after his third marriage he contracted pneumonia and died peacefully at his home on December 19th, 1915. He was buried in the same grave as "Mally", his second wife, at Rake Lane Cemetery, Wallasey.

His death in 1915 marked the end of an era in dialect writing, as, indeed, the war, which was then raging brought to an end the social order of which Hartley was so much a part. Reading his works today is to enter that world again and recapture the spirit of his age, its supreme optimism and confidence even in misery and deprivation. In his life and works, Hartley shares with Dickens the same restlessness and capacity for caricature; there is always an element of the showman in his work as in his life; there is always a concern for the underprivileged and a dislike of the hypocritical and arrogant; there is always a philosophy of life that is optimistic and positive, if at times sentimental, a philosophy expressed in pithy dialect which loses out when turned into standard English.

The grotesque and humorous entered his private life, too, and much of his writing is really an imaginative extension of his life experience. That first trip to America, recorded in "Grimes' Trip to America", was in itself a caricature of life. There were larger than life incidents he experienced which he does not record in his book. In Montreal, for example, he took many jobs, one of which was theatre-manager. On one occasion he booked a troupe of trapeze artists to appear at his theatre and after their performance, as he was going his rounds prior to shutting up the theatre for the night, he noticed the trapeze hooked to the gallery as the acrobats had left it. On impulse, he thought he would have a go and swing across to the stage and back. He unhooked the trapeze and took off, but to his dismay, on the return journey the trapeze failed to reach the gallery. He remained stranded all night on the trapeze till he was rescued!

His pen captures all walks and attitudes of life in the West Riding, and for the social historian his essays and almanac anecdotes provide a rich source for serious study of 19th century Yorkshire. In a cynical age such as ours, which has tended more and more to emphasise the grimness of life in 19th century towns, and the squalor of the workers, Hartley presents us with a spectacular richness of life nurtured by the workers themselves underneath the social conditions in which they lived and worked. Every town and community in the West Riding had its dialect poet, expressing in the local tongue the feelings and attitudes of the communities in which they lived – from Doncaster and Sheffield in the east to small mill towns like Keighley in the west. Many of these poets lived as colourful a life as Hartley himself. William Wright of Keighley, for example, known locally as Bill o'th'Hoylus End, lived in the Bohemian style, travelling far outside his native regions; dressing eccentrically and living life to the full with all the extravaganza of the born showman once he returned and settled down to pen dialect verse about the people and conditions in his home town.

But John Hartley's writing is more than social history. His prose style has a quality, which raises it well above the level of the hack dialect-writers of his day. There is, at times, classical balance and a masterly choice of words in his work; as at the beginning of his essay on "Fooils" (which is included in the selection of his prose later) or in his short article on "September Games", also included, and which reveals the craftsman's development of subject matter and character. Few dialect-writers of his day matched his command of humour. None, I believe, his output. There is a quality in Hartley's dialect-writings which ought to give them a special place in English literature, a place which has not yet been given the accord it deserves; for among the dialect almanac writers of his day, he is without equal.

*Selections from the poetry
of John Hartley*

# TH' FIRST O' TH' SOOART
## (OR PARSON DREW OF PUDSEY.)

Aw heeard a funny tale last neet –
Aw couldn't howd fro' laffin –
'Twor at th' Bull's Heead we chonced to meet,
An' spent an haar i' chaffin.
Some sang a song, some cracked a joak,
An' all seem'd full o' larkin;
An' th'raam wor blue wi' bacca smook,
An' ivvery e' e' d a spark in.

Long Joa 'at comes thro th' Jumples cluff,
Wor getting rather mazy;
An' Warkus Ned had supped enuff
To turn their Betty crazy;
An' Bob 'at lives at th' Bogeggs Farm,
Wi' Nan throo th' Buttress Bottom,
Wor treating her to summat warm,
(It's just his way – "odd drot 'em !")
An' Jack o' th' Slade wor theear as weel,
An' Joa o'Abe's throo Waerley;
An' Lijah, off o' th' Lavvar Hill,
Wor passing th' ale raand rarely.
Throo raand and square they seemed to meet,
To hear or tell a stoory,
But th' gem o' all aw heard last neet
Wor one bi Dooad o' th' Gloory.

He bet his booits 'at it wor true,
An' all seemed to believe him;
Tho' if he'd lost he needn't rue –
But 't wodn't ha' done to grieve him.
His uncle lived i' Pudsey taan,
An' practised local praichin;
An' if he're lucky, he wor baan
To start a schooil for taichin.

But he wor taken varry ill;
He felt his time wor comin,
(They say he brought it on hissel
Wi' studdyin his summin.)
He called his wife and neighbours in
To hear his deein sarmon,
An' tell'd 'em if they lived i' sin
Ther lot ud be a warm un.

Then turnin raand unto his wife
Said – "Mal, tha knows, owd craytur,
If awd been bless'd wi' longer life
Aw might ha' left things straighter.
Joa Sooitill owes me eighteen pence –
Aw lent him it last lovefeast.
Says Mal – "He hasn't lost his sense,
Thank God for that at least!"

"An' Ben o' th' top o' th' bank, tha knaws,
We owe him one paand ten –"
"Just hark!" says Mally, "theear he goas,
He's ramellin agean!
Dooan't tak a bit o' noatice, fowk,
Yo see, poor thing, he's ravin!
It cuts me up to hear sich talk-
He spent his life i' savin."

"An' Mally, lass," he said agean,
"Tak heed o' my direction,
Th' schooil owes us hawf a craan – aw mean
My share o' th' last collection.
Tha'll see to that, an' have what's fair
When my poor life is past."
Says Mally, "Listen, aw declare
He's sensible to th' last."

He shut his een an' sank to rest –
Deeath seldom claimed a better;

23

They put him by – but what were best,
He sent 'em back a letter,
To tell 'em all haa he'd goan on,
An' haa he gate to enter;
An' gave 'em rules to act upon
If ivver they should venture.

Theear Peter stood wi' keys i' hand:
Says he, "What do you want, sir?
If to goa in – yo undersand –
Unknown to me, yo can't, sir.
Pray what's your name? Where are yo throo?
Just make your business clear."
Says he, "They call me Parson Drew,
Aw've come throo Pudsey here."

"You've come throo Pudsey, do you say?
Doan't try sich jokes o' me, sir!
Aw've kept these doors too long a day,
Aw can't be fooiled bi thee, sir."
Says Drew, "Aw wodn't tell a lie,
For th' sake o' all ther's in it;
If yo've a map of England by,
Aw'll show yo in a minit."

Soa Peter gate a timetable –
They gloored o'er th' map together;
Drew did all 'at he wor able,
But couldn't find a stiver.
At last says he, "Theear's Leeds Taan Hall,
An' thear stands Bradforth mission;
It's just between them two – that's all –
Your map's an old edition.

But thear it is, aw'll lay a craan,
An' if yo've nivver knawn it,
Yo've missed a bonny Yorksher taan,
Tho' many be 'at scorn it."

He oppen'd th' gate; says he, "It's time
Somebody coom, aw'll trust thee.
But tha'll find inside noa friends o' thine –
Tha'rt th' first 'at's come throo Pudsey!"

# PLENTY O' BRASS.

Aa! It's grand to ha' plenty o' brass!
It's grand to be able to spend
A trifle sometimes on a glass
For yorsen, or sometimes for a friend;
To be able to bury yor neive
Up to th' shackle i' silver an' gowd,
An', baat pinchin, be able to save
A wee bit for th'time when yor owd.

Aa! It's grand to ha' plenty o' brass!
To be able to set daan yor fooit
Withaat ivver thinkin', bi th'mass,
'At yor wearin' soa mitch off yor booit;
To be able to walk along th' street,
An' stand at shop windows to stare,
An' net ha' to beat a retreat
If yo scent a bum-bailey i' th'air.

Aa! It's grand to ha' plenty o' brass!
To be able to goa hoam at neet,
An' sit i' th' arm-cheer bi th' owd lass,
An' want nawther foir nor leet;
To tak th' childer a paper o'spice,
Or a pictur' to hing up o' th' wall
Or a taste of a summat 'at's nice
For yor friends, if they happen to call.

Aa! it's grand to ha' plenty o' brass!
Then th' parson 'll knaw where yo live;
If yo'r poor, it's mooast likely they'll pass,
An' call where fowk's summat to give.
Yo' may have a trifle o' sense,
An' yo' may be both upright an' true,
But that's nowt, if yo can't stand th' expense
Ov a hoal or a pairt ov a pew.

Aa! it's grand to ha' plenty o' brass!
An' to them fowk 'at's getten a hoard,
This world seems as smooth as a glass,
An ther's flaars o'boath sides o' th' road;
But him 'at's as poor as a maase,
Or, happen, a little i' debt,
He mun point his noas up to th' big haase,
An' be thankful for what he can get.

Aa! it's grand to ha' plenty o' chink!
But doan't let it harden yor heart;
Yo' 'at's blessed wi' abundance should think
An' try ta do gooid wi' a part;
An' then, as yor totterin' daan,
An' th' last grains o' sand are i' th' glass,
Yo' may find 'at yo've purchased a craan
Wi' makkin gooid use o' yor brass.

# Bite Bigger.

As aw hurried throo th' taan to mi wark,
(Aw wur lat, for all th' whistles had gooan)
Aw happened to hear a remark,
'At ud fotch tears throo th' heart of a stooan;
It wur raainin, an' snawin an' cowd,
An' th' flagstooans wur covered wi' muck,
An' th' east wind booath whistled an' howled,
It sanded like nowt but ill luck.

When two little lads, donned i' rags,
Baght stockins or shoes o' ther feet,
Coom trapesin away ower th' flags,
Booath on 'em soddened wi' th' weet.
Th' owdest mud happen be ten,
Th' young un be hauf on't, noa mooar;
As aw looked on, aw sed to misen,
"God help fowk this weather 'at's poor!"

Th' big un sammed summat off th' grand,
An' aw looked just to see what 't could be;
'Twere a few wizened flaars he'd faand
An' they seemed to ha' filled him wi glee,
An' he said, "Come on, Billy, may be
We shall find summat else by an' by,
An' if net, tha mun share thease wi' me
When we get to some spot wheear it's dry."

Leet-hearted they trotted away,
An' aw followed, 'cos 'twere i' mi rooad,
But aw thowt aw'd ne'er seen sich a day –
It worn't fit ta be aht for a tooad.
Sooin big un agean slipped away,
An' sammed summat else aht o' th' muck,
An' he cried aht, "Look here, Bill, today.

Aren't we blessed wi' a seet o'gooid luck?
Here's a apple! An' mooast on it's sand,
What's rotten aw'll thraw into t' street,
Worn't it gooid to lig thear to be faand?
Nah booath on us con have a treat."
Soa he wiped it, an' rubbed it, an' then
Said, "Billy, thee bite off a bit.
If tha hasn't been lucky thisen,
Tha shall share wi' me sich as aw get."

Soa th' little un bate off a touch,
T' other's face beamed wi' pleasure all through,
An' he said, "Nay, tha hasn't ta' en mich,
Bite agean, an' bite bigger, nah do!"
Aw waited to hear nowt noa more –
Thinks aw, thear's a lesson for me!
Tha's a heart i' thi breast, if tha'rt poor,
Th' world were richer wi' more sich as thee!

Tuppince were all th'brass aw had,
An' aw'd meant it for ale when come nooin,
But aw thowt aw'll goa give it yon lad,
He desarves it for what he's been doin.

Soa aw said, "Lad, here's tuppince for thee,
For thisen," – an' they stared like two geese;
But he said, woll th'tear stood in his e'e,
"Nay it'll just be a penny a piece."
"God bless thi! Do just as tha will,
An' may better days speedily come;
Tho' clammed, an' hauf donned, mi lad, still
Tha'rt a deal nearer Heaven ner some."

# A HAWPOTH.

Whear is thi Daddy, doy? Whear is thi Mam?
What are ta cryin for, poor little lamb?
Dry up thi peepies, pet. Wipe thi wet face;
Tears o' thi little cheeks seem aat o'place.
What do they call thi, lad? Tell me thi name;
Have they been ooinin thi? Why, it's a shame!
Here, tak this hawpny, an' buy thi some spice,
Rocksticks or humbugs or summat 'at's nice.
Then run off hoam agean, fast as tha can;
Thear, tha'rt all reight agean, run like a man.

He wiped up his tears wi' his little white brat,
An' he tried to say summat, aw couldn't tell what;
But his little face breetened wi' pleasure all through –
Ah, it's cappin, sometimes, what a hawpny can do!

# COME THI WAYS.

Bonny lassie, come thi ways,
An' let us go together!
Tho' we've met wi' stormy days,
Ther'll be some sunny weather;
An' if joy should spring for me,
Tha shall freely share it;
An' if trouble comes to thee,
Aw can help to bear it.

Tho' thi mammy says us nay,
An' thi dad's unwillin;
Wod ta have mi pine away
Wi' this love 'at's killin?
Come thi ways, an' let me twine
Mi arms once more abaat thee,
Weel tha knaws mi heart is thine,
Aw couldn't live withaat thee.

Ivvery day an' haar 'at slips,
Some pleasure we are missin,
For those bonny rooasy lips
Aw'm nivver stalled o' kissin;
If men wor wise to walk life's track
Withaat sich joys to glad 'em,
He must ha' made a sad mistak
'At gave a Eve to Adam.

# AHR MARY'S BONNET.

Hev ye seen ahr Mary's bonnet?
It's a stunner an' noa mistak,
Ther's a bunch o' roases on it,
An' a feather dahn her back,
Yeller ribbon an' fine laces,
An' a cock-o-doodle doo,
An' araand her bonny face
Is a string o' posies blue.

When shoo went ta chu'ch last Sunda,
Parson couldn't finnd his text,
An' fat owd Mrs Grundy said,
"Ah, Mary, pray what next?"
T' lads winked at one another,
T' lasses sniggered i' ther glee,
An' th' whooal o' t' congregation
Hed her bonnet i' ther e'e.

Then t' choir started singin,
An' th' fust hymn 'at they sang
Wer all abaat the flaars
Of fifty summers gone.
An' when they saw ahr Mary,
They made a mullock on it;
For they thowt 'at all them flaars
Hed bin put on Mary's bonnet.

Then t' parson said most kindly,
Ther wer noa offence intended,
That flaar-shows wer aat o' place
In chu'ch wheer saints attended;
An' if his errin' sister
Wished ta find her way to Glory,
Shoo shouldn't carry on her head
A whoal consarvatory.

Nah ahr Mary isn't short o' pluck,
Shoo jumped up in a minnit;
Shoo looked es if sha'd swallered t' chu'ch
An' ivvery body in it!
"Parson," shoo said, "yer heead is bare,
Nowt in it an' nowt on it,
Suppose yer put some flaars theer,
Like theas 'at's on my bonnet."

(There is some doubt about Hartley's authorship of this poem and I must record that I have not seen it in any of his collections of verse. However, the dialect is certainly that of Hartley's area and the orthography is close to that which Hartley uses. Elderly dialect-reciters in the 1960's who knew Hartley when he was alive also attributed it to him and assured me he wrote it.)

# AGHT O' WARK.

Aw've been laikin for ommost eight wick,
An' aw can't get a day's wark to do!
Aw've trailed abaght th' streets wol aw'm sick
An' aw've worn mi clog-soils ommost through.

Aw've a wife an' three childer at hooam,
An' aw knaw they're all lookin at th' clock,
For they think it's high time aw should come,
An' bring 'em a morsel o' jock.

A'a dear! It's a pitiful case
When th' cupboard is empty an' bare;
When want's stamped o' ivvery face,
An' yo haven't a meal yo can share.

Today as aw walked into th' street,
Th' squire's carriage went rattlin past;
An' aw thowt 'at it hardly looked reight,
For aw hadn't brokken mi fast.

Them horses, aw knew varry weel,
Wi' ther trappins all shinin i' gowd,
Had nivver knawn th' want of a meal,
Or a shelter to keep 'em thro' th' cowd.

Even th' dogs have enough an' to spare,
Tho' they ne'er worked a day i' ther life;
But ther maisters forget they should care
For a chap 'at's three bairns an' a wife.

They give dinners at th' hall ivvery neet,
An' ther's carriages standin bi' th' score,
An' all th' windows are blazin wi' leet,
But they seldom gi' dinners to th' poor.

34

I' mi pocket aw haven't a rap,
Nor a crust, nor a handful o' mail;
An' unless we can get it o' th' strap,
We mun pine, or mun beg, or else stail.

But hoamwards aw'll point mi owd clogs
To them three little lambs an' ther dam;
Aw wish they wor horses or dogs,
For it's nobbut poor fowk 'at's to clam.

But they say ther is one 'at can see,
An' has promised to guide us safe through;
Soa aw'll live on i' hoaps, an' surelee
He'll find a chap summat to do.

# The New Year's Resolve.

Says Dick, "Ther's a notion sprung up i' mi yed,
For th'fust time i' th' whoal course o' mi life,
For aw've taken a fancy aw'st like to be wed,
If aw knew who to get for a wife.

Aw doan't want a woman wi' beauty nor brass,
For aw've nawther to booast on misel;
What aw want is a warm-hearted, hard-workin lass,
An' ther's lots to be fun, aw've heard tell.

To be singel is all weel enough nah an' then,
But it's awk'ard when th' weshin day comes;
For aw nivver think soapsuds agree weel wi' men,
They turn all mi fingers to thumbs.

An' aw'm sure it's a fact, long afoor aw get done,
Aw'm slopped throo mi waist to mi fit;
An' th' floor's in a pond, as if th' peggy-tub run,
An' mi back warks as if it 'ud split.

Aw fancied aw'st manage at breead-bakin best,
Soa one day aw bethowt me to try,
But aw gate soa flustered, aw ne'er thowt o' th' yeeast,
Soa aw mud as weel offered to fly.

Aw did mak a dumplin, but a'a dearie me!
Abaght that lot aw hardly dar think;
Aw ne'er fan th' mistak till aw missed th' sooap, yo see,
An' saw th' suet i' th' sooap-box o' th' sink.

But a new-year's just startin, an' soa aw declare
Aw'll be wed if a wife's to be had;
For mi cloas is soa ragged aw'm ommost hawf bare,
An' theas mullocks, they're drivin me mad.

Soa, if yo should knaw or should happen hear tell
Of a lass 'at to wed is inclined,
Telegraft me at once, an' aw'll see her misel
Afore shoo can alter her mind.

# WAYVIN MEWSIC.

Ther's mewsic i'th'shuttle, i'th'loom, an' i'th'frame,
Ther's melody mingled i'th'noise,
For th'active ther's praises, for th'idle ther's blame,
If they'd hearken to th' saand of its voice;
An' when flaggin a bit, ha refreshin to feel
As yo pause an' look raand on the throng,
At the clank o'the tappet, the hum o'th wheel,
Sing this plain unmistakable song:

> Nick a ting, nock a ting,
> Wages keep pocketing,
> Workin for little is better nor laiking;
> Twist an' twine, reel an' wind,
> Keep a contented mind,
> Troubles are oft of a body's own making.

To see workin fowk wi' a smile o' ther face
As they labour thear day after day,
An' hear th'women's voices float sweetly through th'place,
As they join in some favourite lay;
It saands amang th' din as the violet seems
'At peeps aght fro th'green dockens among,
An' spreading a charm ower th'rest by sich means,
Thus it blends i' that steady owd song:

> Nick a ting, nock a ting,
> Wages keep pocketing,
> Workin for little is better nor laiking;
> Twist an' twine, reel an' wind,
> Keep a contented mind,
> Troubles are oft of a body's own making.

An' then see what lessons are laid out anent us,
As pick after pick follows time after time,
An' warns us tho' silent to let nowt prevent us
From strivin by little endeavours to climb;

38

Th'world's made o' trifles, its dust forms a mountain,
Soa nivver despair as you're trudgin along;
If troubles will come an' your spirit dishearten,
Yo'll finnd ther's relief i' that steady owd song:

>Nick a ting, nock a ting,
>Wages keep pocketing,
>Workin for little is better nor laiking;
>Twist an' twine, reel an' wind,
>Keep a contented mind,
>Troubles are oft of a body's own making.

Life's warp comes throo Heaven, th'weft's fun bi us sen,
To finish a piece we're compelled to ha' booath;
Th'warp's reight, but if th'weft should be faulty – ha then?
Noa wayver i'th'world can produce a gooid cloth.
Then let us endeavour, bi workin and strivin,
To finish awr piece soa's noa fault can be fun,
An' then i' return for awr pains an' contrivin'
Th'takker-in'll reward us an' whisper, "Weel done."

>Clink a clank, clink a clank,
>Workin withaat a thank
>May be awr fortun – if soa nivver mind it,
>Strivin to do awr best,
>We shall be reight at last,
>If we lack comfort nah, then we shall find
>it.

# TAKE HEART!

Roughest roads, we often find,
Lead us on to th'nicest places;
Kindest hearts oft hide behind
Some o'th' plainest-lookin faces.

Flaars whose colours breetest are
Oft delight awr wond'ring seet;
But ther's others, humbler far,
Smell a thaasand times as sweet.

Birds o'monny coloured feather
Please us as they skim along,
But ther charms all put together
Connot equal th'skylark's song.

Bonny women – angels seemin –
Set awr hearts an' brains o'fire;
But it's net ther beauty beamin',
It's ther gooidness we admire.

Th'bravest man 'at's in a battle
Isn't allus th'fust i'th'fray;
He best proves his might an' mettle
Who remains to win the day.

Monkeys an' vain magpies chatter,
But it doesn't prove 'em wise;
An' it's net wi' noise an' clatter
Men o' sense expect to rise.

'Tisn't them 'at promise freely
Are mooast ready to fulfill;
'Tisn't them 'at trudge on dreely
'At are last to th'top o'th'hill.

Bad hawf-craans may pass as payment,
Gaudy flaars awr e'en beguile;
Women may be loved for raiment,
Show may blinnd us for a while.

But we sooin grow discontented,
An' for solid worth we sigh;
An' we learn to prize the jewel,
Tho' it's hidden from awr eye.

Him 'at thinks to gather diamonds
As he walks along his road,
Nivver need be tired wi' huggin,
For he'll have a little load.

Owt 'at's worth a body's winnin
Mun be toiled for long an' hard;
An'tho' th' struggle may be pinnin',
Perseverance wins reward.

Earnest thowt, an' constant strivin
Ever wi' one aim i'th'seet;
Tho' we may be lat arrivin',
Yet at last we'st come in reight.

He who will succeed, he must,
When he's bid false hopes farewell,
If he firmly fix his trust
In his God an' in hissel.

*Selections from the prose of John Hartley*

The following excerpts from Hartley's book "Grimes's Trip to America", told as a series of letters back to a friend in England, capture the flavour of life in Canada and the States during Hartley's first trip to America between 1872 and 1875. The letters are written to John Jones Smith and Hartley uses the pseudonym Sammywell Grimes. The Ananias referred to is an American friend of Hartley who shared his experiences in that first trip and who subsequently returned to England to lecture. The first letter quoted describes life in Quebec.

## LETTER NO. 3 (MONTREAL)

".....We went back to us lodgins an' they showed us whear we'd to sleep. It wor one raam divided bi a wooden partition just high enuff to peep ower, an' a little bed o'each side. We bid one another gooid neet, an' aw lit mi pipe an' sat daan o'th'edge o'th'bed to think things ovver. Aw felt loanly withaat Mally an'th'childer, an' aw thowt a gooid deal abaat thee an' Mistress Smith. Mi first day in a strange country had been one o' disappointment, an' aw think aw should ha' gooan to bed wi' a leeter heart if aw'd knawn aw should ha' been rung up to mi wark o'th'Monday morning.

Aw did fall asleep, but it wor nobbut for a few minnits, for aw'd bargained to hev a bed to misen but aw sooin discovered 'at aw hadn't. Aw tried to settle daan but aw couldn't, for aw mud awther get up or be worried. Ananias wor snoorin o'th'other side o'th'screen, an' ivverybody i'th'haase wor i' bed, soa aw pooled up a cheer to th'winder an' pearked misen o'th'back, wi' mi feet o'th'seeat, an' prepared to watch th'sun rise. Aw suppooas aw fell asleep, for th'next thing aw knew wor, aw thowt som'dy'd hit me wi' a load o'bricks an' ommost brokken ivvery booan i' mi skin.

Ananias jumped aght o'bed an' bobbed his head ovver th'booards an' axed what wor to do.

"It's thease infernal what-do-yo-call-ems," aw sed. "Why, they're as big as little raisins, an' th'bed swarms wi' em!"

"You must have got them bad, partner, if they've thrown you out of bed so unceremoniously."

44

"Tha knaws more abaat thease things nor aw do; soa just com' an' see if tha can help me ony."

He wor sooin pairt donned, an' when aw telled him ha it had happened, he did nowt but laugh an' sed aw should sooin get used to 'em, an' aw worn't to let sich little things bother me. "Well, if them's what tha calls little things," aw sed, "Aw hooap awst nivver see ony big uns, for aw call them flaysome." Then he reminded me ha thankful aw owt to be 'at aw'd tummeld backward, for if aw'd wolted forrard aw should ha' goan through th' winder daan into th'street, an' he assured me 'at a deead Yorkshireman worn't mich thowt on.

As aw declared aw wodn't risk gooin to bed agean he decided to sit up an' have a smook to keep me comp'ny, an' he fished a bottle aght o' one of his pockets, an' after takkin a gooid swig he handed it to me to tak a "eye-opener" as he called it. Then he began tellin me 'at aw should meet wi' things a deal war when we gat into th'States. "What you see here," he said, "arn't a circumstance compared with what you'll find there. Why, some people take a fancy to keep them as pets, and they get so large that they have to cut a hole in the bottom of the door for them to creep in and out, and they wodn't have one killed on my account."

"They sooin wod have if aw wor theear!"

"That's where you'd make a mistake. They are most affectionately disposed towards each other and if you kill one, all its relatives from far and near come to pay their last respects at the funeral and very often invite themselves to remain. And remember what the poet says, 'Take not the life thou canst not give, For all things have a right to live.'"

"That poet's a fooil like thee! Tha'rt just tawkin for tawkin's sake, an' if tha can't oppen thi math withaat letting a lie roll aght, keep it shut."

After passin th'bottle backwards an' forrards a few times, we gate weshed an' donned, an' as we could hear fowk stirrin daanstairs we went aght for a stroll before braikfast.

Th' mornin wor lovely, an' farther we gate away throo th'city, better it lewked, wol we'd getten to whear we could nobbut just see it as throo a mist, th'glitterin spires an' domes, an' th'queer nooks an' corners 'at aw'd been soa disgusted wi', made up one o'th'mooast fairylike picturs aw ivver clapped e'en on, an' aw can easily understand fowk praisin it up as they have done if they've nivver been in it. We sat daan to rest an' enjoy th'pure mornin air, an' we were sooin joined bi a man an' his wife 'at had come ovver i'th'same ship, an' they were i' sad trouble for they'd lost ther purse an'th'bit o'brass they had in it an' ther rail tickets to New York.

We felt varry sorry for 'em, an' as nawther Ananias nor me cared to goa to New York just then, we let 'em have awr tickets an' decided to go to Montreal, whear aw am nah. Ananias sed he had a bit o'business 'at he could do there, an' aw thowt aw should stand just as gooid a chonce o' gettin a job here as onywhere else. We went back to braikfast, an' after that we paid th'shot; an' after gettin th'bit o' brass aw had changed into Canadian paper we spent some time i' buyin a few things aw'd need on, an' aw didn't finnd 'em soa varry dear as aw'd been led to expect. We then bowt tickets for Montreal an' went on booard th'steeambooat. To say it were a flooatin palace willn't give mich idea what it wor. Th' fare were three dollars 50 cents apiece, an' we'd a dinner thrawn in. Aw'd nivver seen owt grander i' mi life, net even i' Lundun, ner that long dining saloon when it were all set aght. Crystal lamps an' beautiful birds i' cages an' baskets o'flaars ivverywhear. Th'cheers were covered wi' crimson velvet, an' there were a carpet 'at let yer feet sink into it as if ye were walkin ovver some fresh faw'n snaw. Th'dinner were fit for a Prince, an' it tewk a gurt weight off my mind, for it were proof 'at there were stuff fit to eyt if a chap could tell whear to get it. Ananias, as usual, made hissen at hooam an' he hadn't been on booard long afore he were walkin wi' th'captain arm i' arm as if there were owd chums. In a bit he put up his finger for me an' introduced me as an owd friend - a manufacturer from Yorkshire! We were invited into th'captain's private office an' had a drop of as gooid brandy as ivver aw tasted. Th'captain then began axin me all sooarts o' questions abaat th'state o' trade, an' aw answered him as truly as aw could; but aw didn't feel comfortable. When he axed me if aw hand't a deeal o' trouble sometimes wi' mi work-people, aw could say "Noa" wi' a clear conscience. He wanted to knaw hah monny mills aw had, an' aw telled him nobbut one – (that's mi coffee-mill 'at stans at th'end o'th'mantleshelf at hooam!).

If aw were a scholar, Smith, aw'd try an' tell thi summat abaat th'scenery on th'St. Lawrence river. Tha knaws aw'm praad o' owd England, but bless thi life! England can booast nowt like this. Th'grandest panorama aw ivver saw i' mi life could noa mooar compare wi' this nor th'Peel Monument can wi' th'Albert Memorial. Ananias an' me sat o'th'upper deck hardly ivver speykin a word wol it were ommost dark, an' when aw went to bed (an' a nice little bed an' bed-room it wor) aw did nowt but dream abaat it. If aw see nowt else, aw shalln't consider it a waste o' brass comin here.

At six o'clock i'th'mornin we landed at Montreal. It's a varry different lewkin place to Quebec. It's summat like a city. Ther's some grand streets here, an' some fine buildings. Ananias went to do his business, an' soa aw went for a stroll through th'streets, but, as aw've mentioned afore, it's soa hot 'at it's ommost past livin aght o' door. Ther's some grand oppen squares, wi' trees an' faantains, an' aw went into one an' sat daan. To pass th'time aw strung together a few lines o' poetry; but if aw put 'em i' this letter it'll mak it aboon weight, soa tha mun wait wol th'next. Trade seems to be varry bad, an' aw'm feeared ther's not mich chonce o' gettin a job; but if nowt turns up aw shall goa wi' Ananias into th'States. Be sewer an' let Mally knaw 'at shoo's noa need to goa into black for me yet.

"SAMMYWELL GRIMES THE ROAMER."

# LETTER NO.4 (NEW YORK, UNITED STATES)

Much of this letter is taken up with describing conditions in Montreal, including the winter there in this vivid piece of descriptive writing.

".....Th'back end o'th'year is what they call th'Indian summer, an' them 'at can enjoy a glorious seet – sich a one as England can nivver show – should goa. Th'mountain 'at rears itsen up at one side o'th'city is covered wi' trees, an' th'grandest colours aw ivver saw cannot come up to th'colours 'at cover it. Th'trees seem to be bowered i' gowd an' scarlet an' purple, an' breeathin th'air is like suppin new milk. This nobbut lasts for two or three weeks, an' then, if yo cannot stand cowd weather yo'd best tak yo'r hook. Aw nivver knew what frost an' snow wer till aw saw it an' felt it theear. All th'cabs an' omnibuses have ther wheels takken off an' goa skatin, an' it's a pity th'poor hosses can't skate, too, for they've a hard time on it. Thirteen feet o' snaw fell while aw wer theear, but it isn't like England snaw, for yo couldn't mak snawballs on it if yo tried, except varry rarely, an' if yo've a fancy to roll in it yo can get up an' shak it off withaat bein even damp. It's a lively seet to walk on Great St. James's Street i' th'afternooin an' see all th' gentry drivin aght i' ther sledges, covered wi' furs an' scarlet rugs, but it's a cowd job unless yer weel lapt up an' have a gooid hot poultice i'yer inside. I'th'market ye find beef, mutton, an'pooark reared up just like as mich timber, an' they break ye a piece off wi' a hammer just as if it wor a lump o' stooan. Ye have to thaw it first an' cook it after. Aw wor standin thear one mornin when as saw a horse an' cart come in an' a chap sat up drivin it, but when th'horse stopped, th'chap didn't offer to stir. When we went to him, we fan him deead wi'th'reins frozzen fast to his hands. If yer aght verry long it isn't at all unlikely yo'll have yer nooas or yer ears frozzen, an' as ye dooan't knaw it yersen, yer rayther capped when a chap comes up to yo wi' a handful o'snaw, an' baat sayin a word, starts o' rubbin yer nooas-end. Th'St.Lawrence is six times th'width o'th'river Thames, but it's just like solid graand. Fowk walk an' drive ovver it as if it wer th'king's high rooad. Spring sets in as sudden as th'winter, an' th' mooast grand thing it's been my lot to see an' hear is th'braikin up o'th' St. Lawrence river. It's just as if scoors o' cannons wor going off at once, an' it seems to shak th'city. Th'ice begins to braik into lumps an' move an' it's a dark lewk aght for owt 'at happens to be in its rooad. Pieces as big as th'front 'th'Bradford Exchange rise up, crushin an' smashin ivverything 'a comes i' ther way; an' th'rooad 'at runs along th'side o'th'river wer piled up as high as a three stooarey haase. Onyboby 'at's a mind to han'l a pick an' spade can get plenty to do at this time, helpin to cleear th'streets, for if they'd to let it thaw, th'city wod be flooded. If a chap cannot live onywhear else, aw should say goa to Montreal; but if he can, it isn't worth his while to change. Wark's scarce, an' if ye get it th'brass doesn't goa as far as it does at hooam; an' as th'citizens are divided into three lots – English, French an' French-Canadians – an' as they hate one another as a dark-complexioned chap is sed to hate holy watter, yo willn't find it varry pleasant. If tha can affoord to goa thear an' tak Mistress Smith for a pleasure trip, shoo'll finnd it's worth th'trouble. But if tha meets onybody 'at tha's ony respect for, 'at's thinkin abaat gooin to mak a livin, tell'em throo me to think twice an' be sure to change ther mind th' second time. Aw nivver warked as hard i' mi life, an' aw nivver made less brass. Aw nivver wor leeter hearted nor when aw turned mi back on it an' started for New York. Aw landed all reight, an' as sooin as aw've hed time to lewk raand aw'll send thi another bit o' news.

Let me remain, agone but not forgetten,

SAMMYWELL.

**P.S.** Whoa does tha think hes just dropped in? Ananias! He says he's been seekin me all throo th' land o' liberty, "that glorious land, bounded on the east by Daybreak, on the west by Eternity Peak, on the north by the Aurora Borealis, and on the south by Eternal Sunshine. "Aw think he's fresh!"

## Letter No. 5. (Philadelphia, Centennial Year)

"......After a varry jolly time in an' araand New York – an' it wor jolly compared to what aw'd gooan through afore, for ther wor plenty o' gooid stuff to ait an' drink – we went to Fall River, Mass, for Ananias had a friend thear 'at he wanted to see. We had to goa in a booat, an' it tewk us all neet, but it's a pleasure to travel here whether yo goa bi land or watter, for ther's ivvery comfort yo can wish for. When we landed, aw can't say aw cared mich for th'lewk o' th'place. It's just abaat like Shelf, an' ther's some rare milns as big as Bottomleys or bigger. Aw saw th'fowk gooin to ther wark, but they dooan't lewk like ther do at hooam; they lewk a varry deeal better. Th'young women wor just dressed as smart as if they wor bonnet makkers, an' th'chaps wor dressed more like book-keepers, an' they didn't shail on i' th'one step today an' another tomorrow style. They just walked as smart as a dyer's seeker-in i' Bradford o' th' market day, an' some on 'em wor even smookin cigars. But if aw spake to ony on 'em it wer th'same tale, "Varry little wark, an' varry little brass." I' New York ther wor 25,000 fowk aght o' wark, an' at Fall River ther wor hundred o' wayvers 'at couldn't get a day's wark to do. Varry few could get more nor two or three days i' th'week. If aw'd had a return ticket aw should ha' fun noa difficulty i' gettin rid on it. Fall River is under th'Maine Liquor Law, an' aw wondered ha Ananias wod get on, for he nivver averaged less nor two 'sensations', as he called 'em, i' th'haar. Aw axed him if he'd browt a bottle.

'A fellow can get as much tanglefoot as he likes here if he hasn't a red cent,' he sed. 'Look y'here.'

He tewk me across th'rooad an' pointed to a winda 'at had nowt in it but a stick o' spice like a child's rockstick, but abaat hawf-a-yard long an' two inch thick. 'Twig?' he sed.

'Well, if that's all they have left, they must hev selled up ommost,' aw replied.

Ananias oppened th'door an' went in. Thear wor th'barcaanter just like a liquor vault at hooam, but noa bottles nor barrels; yet th'chaps wer stood thear an' if

50

they'd nowt ony stronger nor a rock-stick to suck, aw'm noa judge o' fizenomony. Ananias called for 'two rye', an' th'chap gave us each a glass, an' poold ahgt a bottle throo under th' caanter. We helped ussen an' paid for it. Yo aren't expected to be long abaat suppin it, soa we put it aght o' th'seet. Ananias left me wol he went to visit his friends, tellin th'landlord 'at aw wor 'solid an' when aw gate chonce aw axed him if it worn't ageean th'law to sell whiskey.

'Course it is, but there's nobody interferes if you do it on the quiet. I sell more now than ever I did, and save the licence money.'

Aw thowt he seemed to be runnin a big risk, but when aw went aght an' had a walk raand, aw saw lots more windas wi' a rockstick in. If aw hadn't lewked into a lot on 'em, aw could hardly believe 'at it could be true, but they all seemed to be doin a thrivin trade. Th'only difference it seems is 'at a chap mun not be seen i'th'streets druffen, or he's sure to get locked up. As they knaw that, if a chap does get more nor he can carry steadily, they allus send someb'dy hooam wi' him. It seems to me to be a genuine permissive bill, for ivverybody has permission to drink just as mich as they can pay for, an' as th'poleece are just as fond of a drop as other fowk, they can act booath blinnd an' deeaf when it suits 'em. Tha may think it saands varry strange, but as aw've seen it wi' mi own e'en aw will believe it.

We didn't stop thear long, an' when we gate back to New York we had a lewk at some o'th'finest buildins, for ther's plenty on 'em. Then we tewk th'ferry to Jersey City an' th'train to Albany. As yo've getten Pullman cars i'th'owd country, it isn't necessary for me to say mich abaat railway travellin, but ther's one thing aw think is worthwhile mentionin. Ther's nivver ony pushin an' thrustin at th'railway stations to get yor tickets, for ther's shops i' different pairts o' th'city whear yo can go an' buy 'em a day or two afore yo want 'em if yo like. As they're gooid for a month it saves a deeal o' bother. Albany reminded me varry mich o' Bradford, an' Troy isn't at all unlike Briggus, an' just abaat as far off.

Aw've nowt particular to say abaat awther on 'em, for Ananias wor varry thrang, soa aw didn't get to see mich; but aw heard a deal abaat th'factrys at Cohoes, whear they mak shawls an' dress goods, as weel as calica, an' aw thowt aw'd like to see 'em. It wor nobbut an haar's ride an' it wer worth th'trouble. Aw've allus felt praad o'th'Saltaire mills, an' aw consider 'em varry handsome; but they're nawther as handsome nor as big as what aw saw here. They're seven or eight stories heigh, an' ther's soa monny towers an' spires abaat 'em 'at they lewk a deeal more like public buildins nor workshops. Th'winda bottoms are filled wi' plants, an' ther's gardens all raand 'em. As far as it's possible to mak a factry lewk ornamental an' comfortable, they've done it.

As aw wer lewkin up at a long chimla, a chap 'at aw hadn't seen says, 'Nah, lad, what's tha think o' that? Ye've nowt to lick that i' Stannin'ley!'

Aw turned raand an' tewk hod of his hand, an' ommost felt as if aw could ha' put him i' mi pocket. It wor th'fust bit o' reight gradely tawk aw'd heeard for a twelvemonth. Aw could tell bi his fustian britches an' his greeasy cap 'at he hadn't bin thear long, but he wor gettin varry nicely into their way, for ommost afore aw'd time to spaik he axed me what aw wor goin to tak. It seems to be th'fust thing i'th'morn an' th'last thing at neet. Soa we went in an' had a drop o soda watter, an' he telled me he'd been thear abaat six months, but trade wer varry slack. Net hawf o'th'machinery wer goin, an' that didn't run hawf o' th' time. Unless ther wor a big alteration i' trade, they wer intendin shuttin up altogether. Ther wor a vast deeal o'want, he telled me, an' hundreds wor thear just becos they couldn't raise th'brass to get away. When trade is gooid it must be a grand place for workin fowk, but just nah, it's as mich as a chap can do to get a livin, an' he's lucky 'at can do that.

Aw went an' met Ananias at neet an' we started for Philadelphia next mornin. When aw write to the' ageean, awst tell the' all abaat th' Centennial Exhibition.

When tha send awr Mally th'news aght o' this letter, tha'd beter net say owt abaat that comic theatre do; net 'at shoo'd care owt abbat it, net shoo marry! But aw think tha'd better net. Tha can tell her 'at aw saw Henry Ward Beecher's chapel if tha likes. Split my kind love between thisen an' Arrybella, an' believe me to be

T'BOTTLE HUGGER TO ANANIAS.

"Friend Smith,

Aw begin to feel thankful 'at aw com here, for if aw hadn't, aw'm sewer aw should ha' missed a deeal 'at's worth hittin. Th'farther aw goa an'th'more capt aw am. New York surprised me aboon a bit, but Philadelphia licks all aw ivver fancied. They call it Quaker City, an' they do reight, for it's just as cleean an' trim lewkin as if it wor a Quaker. Th'fust thing 'at struck me when aw left th' train wor Ananias's thirst, for, as usual,, he wor dry an' wanted to call mi attention to a place whear he could leck on. Th'next thing wor th'width o'th'streets; ommost all on 'em as straight as an arrow, an' th'beauty o'th'buildins. Ivverything lewks as cleean an' neeat as if ther wor nawther dust nor smook. Th'haases are mooastly built o' red brick, an' th' door jawms an' th' steps an' th'winda bottoms are all i' white marble. Walnut Street, Chestnut Street an' Market Street cannot be licked bi owt tha showed mi i' Lundun, an' th' shops are handsomer, takkin 'em all together, nor ony aw ivver saw afore. Some on 'em are built o' white marble an' ommost covered wi' ornaments. When aw walk past an' se th'show o' stuff o' ivvery side, th'width o' th' street an' th'craads o' weel-dressed fowk, aw can hardly wonder at th' pride they feel i' what they are an' what they hev. Of cooarse, one o' th'fust things we'd to goa an' see wor th'Exhibition. Soa we gat into a street car an' started off for Fairmount Park, which is booath bigger an' grander nor th'Central park i' New York. Tha can form a bit of a nooation o'th'size on it when aw tell thi it's a nine-mile walk throo end to end. Th'river Schuylkill runs through it an' is dotted wi' booats, little an' big, an' then ther are shady walks an' summer haases whear yo can rest. Ther are hills yo can climb an' get views 'at cannot be described wi' pen an' ink. Trees an' flaars an' faantains surraand ye ivverywhear an' set yo thinkin 'at if th'Garden o' Eden wor hawf as hansom, it's a thaasand pities 'at Mistress Eve wor created wi' a taste for raw apples. Th'Exhibition itsen rayther knocked consait aght o'mi, for although aw'd expected finndin it a big un – for they seeamto goa in for ivverything big i' this country – yet aw worn't prepared to finnd it owt like as big as it is. Why, ther's monny a taan at hooam 'at sends two members to Parliament 'at doesn't stand o' onny more graand. Even Ananias seemed a bit capt, an' it isn't a little thing 'at can cap him. We walked past two or three big buildins, ony on 'em big enough for an exhibition, an' aw began to wonder if he meant to goa in, or whether he'd keep p'radin abaat all th' day; but when aw saw a smile creeap ovver his face an' he started off like a shot, aw mud ha' knawn, if aw'd gi'en it a thowt, what he wor huntin after. We sooin landed in a place whear hundreds o' thirsty souls wor callin aght for 'cocktails', 'mint juleps', 'stone walls', 'brandy smashers', 'crusade cordial' and scoors o' sich like. Ananias swallowed an 'eye-opener' an' aw hed a 'ginsling', an' then he called for a powder flask, which turned aght to be a bottle o' whiskey. As sooin as aw'd getten it i' mi pocket, he made a start to see what wor to be seen.

To offer to tell what we did see wod be just abaat as interestin as reeadin a dickshunary. As tha's seen exhibitions at hooam tha can form a varry gooid idea what it's like. Exhibitions allus seem to me varry mich like ovvergrown brokers' shops, but ther's just one thing ' at aw may mention, an' that is, th'fowk i'th' owd country 'at place soa mich faith i'th'betterness o' ther awn stuff, an' fancy 'at Yankees are a long way behind 'em, wod be vary likely to alter ther noashuns if they knew more abaat it. Carpets an' damasks are quite gooid as owt aw've ivver seen at hooam, an' hardwares o'ivvery sooart is a match for owt 'at's turned aght o' Sheffield. We spent two whole days i' gapin abaat, an' when we left it we'd seen varry little indeed compard wi' what wor to be seen. We met lots o'English fowk, an' they wor easy to tell, for they dooan't seem to have th'knack o' makkin thersen at hoam. Aw wor varry quiet, for aw couldn't get a chance to speeak 'cos Ananias had soa mich to say. He wor just like a walkin guide-book. Aw nivver met wi' a chap 'at had sich a gift o' th'gab i' mi life. Aw felt reight stalled aght when we sat daan at a fust-rate supper at th'Continental Hotel. It's a slap up shop, an' aw should call it varry expensive, but Ananias says a thing's cheeap enough if it's worth it. He left mi in a bitto amuse misen as best aw could wol he went after a bit o' business of his awn. Aw lit mi pipe (an' aw may jist mention here 'at aw've nivver had a bit o' daycent bacca sin aw coom, for it's all like smookin leead pencil cuttins) an' aw strolled aght wonderin what to do wi' misen.

As aw wor passin a big buildin, aw saw a lot o' fowk craadin raand th'door, an' a big bill 'at wor pasted sed ther wor going to be a teetotal lectur. As th'front seeats wor nobbut twenty five cents an' th' back seeats wor free, aw thowt aw'd speklate o' one o'th'back seeats, for aw wor feelin varry tired an' aw mud as weel sit daan thear for an haar or two as goa rammellin abaat th'streets. After a bit o' thrustin aw gate inside, an' a rare hoilful ther wor. Aw managed to get into a corner, an' aw wor just gettin ready for a bit of a sleep, when th' lecturer made a beginin. Aw couldn't see him throo whear aw sat, but aw ommost jumped aght o' mi skin. Aw wor sewer aw couldn't be mista'en wi' that voice soa aw stood up o'th'seeat to get a gooid lewk at him. Aw rubbed mi een an' blew mi nooas to mak sewer aw worn't asleep, but aw couldn't be mistakken. Aw wor wide awake an i' mi senses. Thear stood – who does ta think? If it worn't Ananias, aw'll be hung!

Mi fust thowt wor to jump daan an' run, but as a chap behind saved me trouble wi' jarkin at mi coit-laps, aw sat daan at th'top of another chap's hat an' decided to wait an' hear what he'd have th' impidence to say. He tawkt for aboon an haar, an' aw nivver heard sich a black nomony abaat 'The Demon Drink' as he gav us, an' aw nivver knew afore 'at drinkin cowd watter wor sewer to mak a chap healthy, wealthy an' wise, as weel as religious an' honest. But he showed it cleear enough 'at if ther wor noa drink i'th'world, ther'd be no more wickedness. Ivverybody'd be prosperous an' happy, th'prisons 'ud have to be turned into hot-pey shops, an' parsons an' policemen 'ud all be aght o' wark. Ha he could fashion to stand up theear wi' a pint o'whisky in his belly, if he'd drop, an' say sich things as he did, aw cannot tell! But it wor evident 'at fowk believed all he sed, for one minnit they must ha' been sooar; then, when he warked hissen into a passion, an' called for 'em all to sign th'pledge afore they went away, for fear they might fill a drunkard's grave if they didn't, ther wor a reg'lar rush up to th'table, an' it tewk three chaps to finnd 'em pens an' paper. Aw wor hawf inclined to goa an' sign missen, but aw thowt if Ananias, 'at knew soa mich more abaat it nor aw did, dar run th'risk of 'The Drunkard's Doom', ther wor noa need for me to be in a hurry......."

# "If Aw Wor a Woman"
## (From "Mally an' Me")

Two of the most loveable characters whom Hartley created were Mally and Sammywell Grimes, based on himself and his second wife. Despite her shrewish tongue, Mally's deep love for her husband is never far from expression; indeed, the constant attack on her husband's failings is really a measure of her great concern for him. In this extract – only just a dialogue! – much of the relationship of Mally and Sammywell is seen, as well as a rich amount of detail of Victorian domestic life in a West Riding working-class home:

"If aw wor a woman aw'd -"

"If tha wor a woman th'd be a disgrace to ivverybody belangin to thi, an' tha'rt little else nah," sed Mally.

"Aw wor goin to remark, 'at if aw wor a woman -"

"Eah! But tha aren't a woman, an' tha wor tha'd wish thisen a man ageean varry sharply. But if aw wor a man aw'd set a different example to what tha does. Aw wonder sometimes what tha'rt thinkin on, if tha ivver does think, which aw'm inclined to daat, unless it's thinkin ha tha contrive to be awkaard an' aggravatin."

"Well, but as aw wor gooin to say, if aw wor a -"

"Aw dooan't want to hear owt tha has to say abaat it. A fine woman tha'd mak! But aw wish tha wor foorced to swap places wi' me for a wick. Aw should like to see ha tha'd fancy gettin up afore dayleet of a Mundy morning an' start o' sich a weshin o' clooas as aw hev to face ivvery wick; to say nowt abaat starchin an' manglin an' ironin. An' then to start an' brew a barrel o' ale for other fowk to sup; an' then to bake – nivver to mention makkin th'beds an' cleeanin th' hearthstun – an'th'meeals to get ready, an' then to cleean th'haase throo top to bottom ivvery wick – an' darn stockins an' put on a claat here an' a patch theear, an' fifty more things beside – an' nivver a word o' thanks for it! Aw just wish tha wor a woman for an odd wick. Aw do, truly!"

"As aw sed afore. If aw wor a -"

"Aw'm capt tha hasn't more sense nor to keep tawkin sich fooilishness. Tha knaws tha aren't a woman an' tha nivver can be – more's th'pity. But if aw wor a man, aw'd awther tawk sense or keep mi maath shut. Aw think sometimes 'at summat'll happen to thi as a judgement for bein sich an ungrateful tyke as tha art. Tha gets up in a mornin an' finnds thi braikfast ready, an' if ther's owt i'th'haase 'at's nice an' tasty tha gets it. Then tha walks aght, an' comes to thi dinner, an' off ageean wol drinkin time, an' after that tha awther gooas an' caars i' some Jerryhoil, or else tha sits rockin thisen i'th'front o'th'foir, smookin thi bacca an' enjoyin thisen wol bedtime. Ther's some fowk dooan't knaw when ther well done to. But aw knaw who it is 'at has to tew an' slave all th'day, wi' hardly a chonce to wipe th'sweeat off mi face."

"But if tha'll lissen, aw wor gooin to remark if aw wor -"

"Tha makes a deeal too monny remarks. Tha'll sit thear remarkin an' praichin bi th'haar together, an' nivver gi' mi a chonce to get a word in edgeways. But aw'm just sick an' stalled o' hearkenin to thi. Ther wor a time, years sin nah – but aw can remember it, tho' tha's forgetten it – when tha used to sit an' lissen to owt aw had to say, an' my word wer law then. An' if mi little finger warked tha'd hardly sleep of a neet for troublin abaat it. But it's different nah. Aw dooan't believe it ud disturb thi if mi heead had to tummel off mi shoolders. Aw've studden a gooid deeal sin aw wor wed to thee, an' aw expect awst ha' to stand a lot more; but one thing aw willn't put up wi', an' that is sittin an' lissenin to thee, an' havin to keep mi tongue still. Soa tha knaws!"

"Well, if aw wor -"

"Nah, let it stop just wheear it is. Tha's getten a tawkin fit on, aw knaw. Aw wonder thi jaws dooan't wark. Aw willn't hear another word! Noa, net a word!"

"But if -"

"Ther's noa 'buts' abaat it. Hod thi noise, do! Tha'd tawk a hen an' chickens to deeath, tha wod. Aw wonder if aw shall ivver hev a bit o' peeace? Net befoor aw'm laid low, an' that's for sure."

AN EXTRACT FROM

## "SAMMYWELL GRIMES AN' HIS WIFE MALLY'S TRIP TO TH'PARIS EXPOSITION AN' THEIR ASCENT OF TH'EIFEL TOWER" (CHAPT. 3).

(In this excerpt from "Mally an' Me" Sammy and his wife are visiting Paris, living at a lodging house there kept by a Bradfordian called Tom.)

".....After dinner aw axt Tom whear he'd advise us to goa for th' afternooin.

'Well,' he sed,' as it's soa varry warm, this ud be a gooid day to goa up th'Tower, for ther's allus a breeze up thear.'

'That's what aw should like,' sed Mally. 'It's mooastly on accaant o' that tower 'at aw've come.'

Aw'd noa objection to mak, soa we steered for it.

Mally had donned her black silk gaan, an' fixt hersen up to th' mark, an' shoo'd getten Tom's wife to but her a parasol, an' aw couldn't help feelin a bit praad o'th'owd lass. A bus coom along wi' a sign 'Eifel Tower', soa we took it an' it put us daan cloise to it. By, but what a monstrous thing it is! It seems to spring off four big arches, two hundred feet heigh, an' to go up wol yo can hardly follo it. It weighs seven thaasand, three hundred tons. Ther wor hundreds o' fowk gooin in, soa we went too. A'a, what a roar a' a rattle ther wor when we gate inside! It sanded ike goin throo Beacon Hill tunnil. We gat tickets an' in we went. Ther wor sactackels to save th'trouble o' climbin up. They could tak up a hundred a time an' they goa up at th'rate of a yard a second. We stopped at th'fust platform, an' here we fun four restaurants. Net little bits o' places, but big roomy places whear hundreds o'fowk wor aitin an' drinkin. Ther wor one for th' French, one for th'Russians, one for th'Flemish, an' th'English an' Americans had another between 'em. We wanted nowt, soa after a gooid look raand, we stepped into th' sactackel ageean an' started for th'top of all. By gow! But we wor scared. Aw could feeal th'whoal thing sway throo side to side like a tree in a wind. Ivvery thing cooms to an end, an' we stopped at last. As we stepped aght, ther wor a gust o'wind at ommost took us off us feet, an' Mally's face wor as white as a lump o' mutton suet. Aw dooan't knaw ha aw looked, but aw knaw ha aw felt. We sat daan for a minnit or two, an' aw could booath feel an' see th'whoal consarn dither an' shak as if it wor ready to topple ower. Mally, as usual, had been varry thowtful an' shoo'd browt a drop o' nerve-reviver wi' her in a bottle. We booath took a swig an' then we felt a bit better for we'd th'pluck to stand up, an' hoddin tight onto th'railins we looked raand.

Th'booats on th'river looked like cockroaches, an' men an' women wor nobbut specks movin along th'streets. It wor a wonderful seet, but mi knees knockt together wol aw couldn't enjoy it, an' we wor varry glad to sit daan ageean. It wor growin varry dark, an' gusts o' wind whistled ivvery nah an' then, an' then, an' black claads coom rollin up. Ther wor ivver sign of a thunner storm. We wor under shelter an' we thowt we'd better wait wol it blew ovver, although fowk wor goin daan as fast as they could tak 'em. Then ther wor a rummel o' thunner an' a flash o' leetin, follered bi another, an' th'rain began to fall like a lot o' glass rods.

"Aw wish we'd come some other day," aw sed.

"It's noa use wishin," sed Mally, "for that willn't help it onny. Aw set mi heart on comin, an' aw'm here, an' if we can nobbut get safe daan ageean, awst be satisfied; but aw'm sewer tha owt to want to stop here, for tha'rt nearer to heaven nah nor tha ivver wor, or ivver will be unless tha alters."

Aw hedn't time to mak onny reply, for a flash o' leetnin ommost blinded us. A crash o' thunner follered 'at shook th'whooal affair, as if it wor a giant tryin to shak it to bits. Flash follered flash, an' sparks an' wavin streeaks o' fire donced abaat th'iron work, makkin it terrible an' grand. Crash after crash o' thunner rockt an' shook th'whooal consarn wol aw felt sewer it wor goin to topple over. Th'rain seemed to coom throo ivver quarter, an' th'gusts o' wind sent it whirlin throo wol we wer as weet as a sop. It nobbut lasted abaat fifteen minnits, but it wor long enough. Ther wor abaat fifty fowk beside us, an' aw nivver saw a more serious-lookin lot o' faces i' mi life. Mally'd shut her een, an' aw could see her lips movin. Aw knew 'at shoo wor prayin for us all.

Sooin th'sun burst aght ageean, th'wind deed away, but th' mighty tower tremmeld an' shook as if conscious of havin coom aght of a desperate struggle. But what a glorious seet it wor nah! Ivverything sparkled an' glittered as if dusted wi' millions o' diamonds. Aw can nivver forget it – nor will Mally. We took us turn to goa daan. We didn't stop at onny o'th'stoppin places. We'd had enough. When we gate daan to solid graand once more, we gave a sigh o' thankfulness an' slowly walked away.

"What's matter wi' thi?" aw sed. "We're safe enough nah."

"It's noan that aw'm thinking abaat. It's this silk gaan 'at's botherin me. Aw've had it for ommost twenty year an' it's nivver been wet befoor. It's sodden throo an' throo. Aw mun get it off an' sponge it an' dry it as straight as aw can. Awr Hepsabah'll goa wrang in her heead if it's spoiled, for aw've promised it her when owt happens to me."

"Neer bother!" aw sed. "Awr Hepsabah can afford to buy one for hersen if shoo wants one."

"Net like this shoo can't! They dooan't mak silks like this nah."

Aw went hooam th'nearest rooad aw knew, an' shoo wor sooin hard at wark i'th'kitchen. Tom's wife an' her seeamed to get on famously together. Th'booarders began to drop in – ther wor abaat a dozen – an' it kept Tom thrang wol they'd finished. Then he called me into th' kitchen, an' th'four on us sat daan to an owd fashioned English drinkin. Tooasted teah cakes an' muffins an' curran cake, an' a big dish full o' lettuce, an' Mally went upstairs an' fotched th'brandy bottle. Shoo wod put us all a drop in us teeah, tho' aw sed, "Pleeas excuse me!" Of course, all th'tawk wor abaat th'Tower but

Tom sed we hadn't hawf seen it. We mud goa an' see it when it wor lit up, but Mally wodn't heear abaat gooin aght ageean that day, soa Tom an' me agreed to have an haar or two, an' tak Mally some other neet.

It wodn't be reight fer me to tell whear we went an' what we did, but we'd a reight gooid do! It wor two o'clock i'th'mornin when we showed up, an' th'only excuse we could mak wor 'at we'd been lost. Aw'm sewer we had, but it wor lost in amazement at what aw'd seen..."

## "Mally's Kursmiss Party"
## (from 'Mally an' Me')

We'd a grand getherin o' relations an' friends, an' when th'table wor set for th'drinkin it looked fit for a feeast for th'lord mayor. Mally's allus been praad o'th'way shoo could provide for a pairty, but this time shoo'd ovver-topt all shoo'd ivver done afore. Ther wor one cake i'th'middle 'at shoo sed wor th'imitation o' Solomon's Temple, an' Solomon wor theear sittin i' all his wisdom aghtside th'front door. Ha he'd ivver getten aght if once he'd been in, or ha he'd gat in nah 'at he wor aght, nubdy but a chap as wide as hissen could tell, for his heead wor six-inch aboon th'temple top, although he wor sittin daan.

Aw ventured to draw Mally's attention to it an' shoo sed shoo'd made him that size because he wor a great man, an' shoo thowt that size wor as big as wod be likely to be etten, soa aw sed noa more abaat it. Ther wor bowls full o'potted mait, an' sandwiches, an' curran cakes, an' funeral bisket, presarves, an' aw dooan't knaw what else, but ther wor enough to puzzle onny body which to start on fust. Ov cooarse, ther wor a sup o' gooid teah, flavoured wi' a drop o' Jamaka creeam (It wodn't do to leave th'creeam aght. A drop o' rum's like as if it sets things gooin a bit, but Mally'd put it in hersel soa's ivvery body'd get a fair share, tho' we hed a drop more i'th'cupboard.). Aw nivver saw a jollier lot sit daan to a drinkin i' mi life.

"What will ta have, Hepsabah?" shoo sed to awr lass. "Tha knaws tha mun get summat into thi, for tha needs it wi' that child to suckle."

"Aw'll look after misen," sed Hepsabah, an' all th'rest sed th' same, an' they started as if they meant it. They tackled th'mooast substantial stuff fust, just to tak th'edge off ther appetites. Then Mally ordered me to sarve aght Solomon's Temple.

"Well, "aw says," aw think aw'll start at th'top stoory fust." Soa aw cut off a lot o' chunks abaat th'size o' bricks, an' to see th' way they wor swollered wor a caution. A'a! What fun ther wor as one ax'd for another chaymer wi' two winders, an' another for th'best paylor, an' they kept me at it wol ther nowt left but th'front door step. Then they grummeled because ther worn't a cellar kitchen.

"What's to become o' poor Solomon, nah?" axed one o' th'naybours. "He looks loansome."

"Ait him an' all!" shaated three or four on 'em.

"He'll feel sadly cut up," aw sed "nah he's lost his temple."

"He'll be war cut up afore we've done wi' him," sed th'wimmen, an' they all passed ther cups for some more teah to swill daan th'last of his habitation.

"Befoor tha starts cuttin it," sed Mally, "just tak them two brace buttons aght at aw put in for een. An' aw'm feeared tha'll finnd his heead rayther soft, for aw wor feeared o' bakin too mich lest aw should spoil his complexion."

"He's noan th'fust 'at's been a bit soft abaat th'heead," aw sed, an' aw made a drive at him.

If ther'd been fun abaat th' temple, it wor nowt compared to th' fun ther wor nah. Th'heead, an'th'shoolders, an'th'breeast, an'th'chine, an' all t'other joints wor called for, until ther wor nowt left but th' hams, an' they sed they'd to be for Mally an' me. Wheearivver they managed to stow all th'stuff aw connot guess, but aw think they must ha' been savin thersen for a wick an' come as hollow as a lot o' drums. But aw wor suited to see 'em enjoyin thersen, an' Mally wor as pleeased an' as praad as if th'queen had paid her a visit. When th' chaps had finished, they all wanted a bit o' bacca, soa aw took 'em into th'wesh-haase, to have a smook wol th'wimmen could mak up ther minds to leeave th'table.

"Nah, as th'fellies have gooan, we'll just ha' a cup to ussen," sed Mally. "Sammy!" shoo said," just raik aght that little bottle o'rum an' we'll have a drop o' extra i' this last cup."

"All reight," aw sed, "aw'll buttle it raand." Soa aw gate it an' shared it amang 'em.

"Nah, lasses," sed Mally. "Here's wishin yo all a Merry Kursmiss an' a Happy New Year, an' aw hooap we shall all live to meet ageean come next Kursmiss."

"Hear, hear!" they all sed, an' they drained off ther cups at a swoller.

When they'd supped up, Mally put her cup daan, an' a queer look coom ovver her face. "Aw dunnot think that tastes as nice as what we hed befoor," shoo sed.

"Noa more do aw," chimed in t'others.

"It's happen too strong," aw sed.

"Ther's a queer flavour abaat it, choose ha," sed Mally, "an' maybe aw forgate to scal'd th'bottle aght befoor th'rum wor put in."

"Why, ther's nowt 'at'll pooisen us," sed her sister Becky, an' aw left 'em to help to side th'pots an' square th'place up a bit. Th'chaps cared varry little ha th'wimen wor gettin on, for they wor enjoyin thersen famously. Two wor astride o'th'wringin machine, an two wor caar'd o' th' set-pot, an' one i' one place an' one in another, an' they wor singin 'Rule Britannia' an' makin enough din to lift th'thack, until owd Amos lost his balance an' fell ovver into th'peggy tub. That stopped th'singin but made more laughin. We managed to hawl him aght, an' then they began tellin tales. They wor all tales we'd heeard scores o' times afore, but we laughed just as mich as if they'd been new, an' time wor passin merrily till Mally coom to th'door an' called for Amos.

"What's up nah?" he axed.

"Come here. Thi wife wants thi," shoo sed.

"Tell her to wait," he sed.

"But shoo connot wait. Shoo's in a hurry," shoo replied.

Soa he went to see what ther wor to do. In abaat a minnit he coom an' sed, "Gooid neet, chaps. Awr Ellen's takken badly an' aw've to tak her hooam."

"It must be Solomon an' her 'at connot agree," sed Lija.

We wor just gettin ready for a bit more spooart, when Mally's face popped in ageean an' aw could see shoo looked scared. Shoo sed Lija wor wanted. He'd hardly getten away when we could hear grooans soa we all jumped up an'

66

follered him. Aw nivver saw a lot o' wimmen change soa i' all mi life an' Mally seemed fair melancholy. Some wor rockin thersen an' lookin as if summat terrible wor gooin to happen. Some wor putting ther bonnets on i' sich a fluster as if they'dan important engagement to keep an' wor feeared they'd be lat.

"Aw believe we're all pooisened!" sed awr Hepsabah; an' aw must say things began to lewk serious when Mally shot past me an' flew daan th'yard. An' when Hepsabah ran off as if to ovvertak her aw didn't knaw what to think. I' three minnits aw'd th'haase to misen. Aw ail'd nowt, an' nooan o'th' chaps seemed to have owt th'matter wi' 'em, an' aw wor puzzlin to finnd aght what it all meant when in come Mally.

"Whativver has ta been doin?" shoo sed.

"Me! Aw've done nowt!" aw replied. "What are ta flyin at me for?"

But shoo didn't fly at me, shoo flew to th' cupboard an' browt aght th'empty bottle. "What does that label say?" shoo sed. Aw sed it all in a minnit. "Tincture o' Rhubub" it sed.

"Eaah, an' tha knew what it wor!" Shoo sed, but shoo ran off ageean to lewk after Hepsabah. Aw went to bed.

Aw wor as innercent as a new-born babby, but aw couldn't mak 'em believe it. It wor a long time befoor some o'th'wimmen wod spaik to me if they met me on th' street; but after a time they seeamed to be willin to lewk over it, for they sed maybe Solomon an' his temple might ha' proved too heavy for ther stummacks. It's all over nah, but aw think yo've heeard enough o' mi trials an' tribulations for one sittin.

## "September Sports"
## ('Clock Almanack' 1916 – the last one edited by Hartley and published posthumously.)

It's a wonderful caanty is Yorksher for spooarts o' all maks – fooitball, an' cricket, an' racin, an' coursin, an' pigeon shooiting, an' boxin, an' – an' aw cannot tell yo what beside, for aw should fill this paper if aw'd to write daan hawf o'th'things 'at shows ha fain th'tykes is for spooart. When bits o' lads fratch i' ther laikin, they dooan't start o' argyfyin, but they shaat aght at once: "Aw'll bet yo a bob it worn't!" Tho' happen ther isn't three aght o'th'lot 'at has a copper to bless hissen wi'.

Aw heard a bit sin abaat a schooil inspector up i' Scammonden, who wor hearin th'childer ther jography. "What are the names of the principal English lakes?" he axed.

"Fooitball laikin, nur an' spell, pitch an' toss an' prize feightin," sed a lad abaat eight-year owd, an' aw dare bet a five paand nooat, if aw had one, 'at Yorksher's th' only caanty i' all England wheear sich a answer could ha' been getten.

# "FOOILS"
## ('YORKSHIRE DITTIES' FIRST SERIES.)

Ther's some born fooils, an' ther's some mak thersen fooils, an' ther's some get made fooils on. When we hear fowk tell tales abaat seein boggards, an' gettin ther planets ruled, we think it saands fooilish. Nah an' then one turns up rayther simple, an' a body con hardly help laughin. It's net long sin aw heeard tell of a owd woman goin to th' pooast office i' Bolton an' axin to see th'maister, an', when he coom, shoo sed shoo wanted to knaw hah monny stamps it 'ud tak to send a mangle to Yeaworth. He couldn't tell her, an' shoo went away thinkin what a fooil he wor net to knaw his business better nor that; an' he thowt what a fooil shoo wor for axin sich a question. An soa it is. We're apt to think ivverybody fooils but ussen an' them 'at belangs to us.

Yo dooan't oft finnd a mother or fayther 'at thinks ther lad's a fooil (unless he gets wed, an' then they allus say so.) Ivverybody's child is th'grandest an' th'cliverest i'th'world. But aw couldn't help laughin one day when aw heeard a chap braggin abaat his lad. "Aa," he sed, "he's cliverest lad of his age aw ivver met. He's nobbut thirteen year owd an' he con do owt!" Just as he wor sayin soa th'lad coom into th'raam, aitin a raw turnip, an his fayther thowt he'd show him off a bit; soa he sed, "Jack, aw want thee to go an' measure t'length o' that piece o' timber 'at's i't'yard, an' coom an' tell me." Soa he gave him his two-fooit rule an' th'lad went. Aw thowt he wor a long time abbat it, but in a bit he coom back. "Well, Jack," sed his fayther, "haa long is it? Spaik up; that's a fine lad."

"Why," he says, "it's th'length o' yor rule, an' my pocket comb, an' this bit o' band."

"That's reight," says his fayther. "Tha can goa hooam." But aw nooaticed 'at he nivver bragged abaat him quite soa mich after that.

## 'Rambling Remarks – March'
### (from the 'Clock Almanack' of 1900.)

Doctors say 'at fowk 'at sleep wi' ther maaths shut live longer nor them 'at sleep wi' 'em oppen, an' aw soppooas they owt to knaw; but aw do knaw 'at fowk 'at keep ther maaths shut when they aren't asleep live a deeal more peaceable lives nor them 'at's too mich gab.

This is a famous month for fooitball laikin. Aw wonder sometimes if it wodn't be a gooid thing if some o' th' fooitball laikers kept ther maaths shut, an' if th'craads 'at goa to watch 'em couldn't keep theirs shut an' all. St Paul says, "It's not what goeth into a man that defiles him, but what cometh out of him." If that's true, some 'at aw've been fooarced to listen to must have a filthy inside. Aw'm too owd to laik at fooitball misen, but aw can remember th'time when aw did, an' even yet, aw'm as fond of aght-door sports as ivver, tho' aw connot tak part in 'em. It's a hard thing to say, but it's true; in a long life of ups an' daans, it's nivver been my lot to listen to as mich cursin, as mich blasphemy, as mich obscene an' filthy tawk as aw heeard at three fooitball matches aw've been at. Aw'm nooan a thin-skinned chap, but if a chap connot goa to see a game played withaat havin to swoller sich a torrent o' vulgarity an' wickedness, aw knaw one 'at'll nivver goa ageean. They say it's a game 'at improves ther muscles, but if they connot improve ther muscles withaat degradin ther morals, th' less we have on it an' better. Ther wor some women theear, but to ther credit be it said, they cried 'Shame!', an' went away as sooin as they could get. Th'brutality an' th' rowdyism 'at follored wer a fittin wind-up to sich a orgy o' filth an' profanity. This didn't tak place i'th' cannible islands, but i'th' bonny green dales o' dear owd Yorksher. Aw hooap at some on 'em 'at took pairt will read this. It's a filthy subject an' aw've touched it as leetly as aw could, but sooiner it's altered an' th'better for th' game an' all consarned. Aw'm thankful to say 'at all fooitball players aren't alike, an' aw knaw some as jolly an' as daycent chaps as yo'll finnd in a day's march.

Owd Jane Slopcot lived at Wilsden, an' shoo'd three lads sich as ony mother wod be praad on. Shoo'd browt 'em up in a reight way, an' shoo'd nivver ony reason to regret it, for they wor as steady as they wor hansom, an' that's net sayin a little. If they had a fault, it wor 'at they wor soa full o' fun woll they wor allus havin a marlock wi' som'dy, an' ther mother coom in for a share. They were all crack fooitballers, but they nivver neglected ther wark ner ther hooam. Th' owdest lad's birthday happen to fall o'th'Sunday, an' as a treeat shoo decided to mak a big birthday puddin. Shoo put th'set-pot on fust thing i'th'morning, an' as sooin as th'watter boiled, shoo put th'puddin in – an' it wor a wopper! Th'lads thowt ther wor a chonce for a bit o' fun, an' as sooin as shoo turned her back, they lifted th'puddin aght an' put a fooitball in, puttin th'lid on to hod it daan. Then they sneeaked off wi'th'puddin to a naybour's haase to get it cooked, for they didn't want to miss it. Owd Jane worn't long afore shoo went to see ha it wor gettin on. 'A'a,' shoo said, 'aw'm feeared aw've made it to leet.' Shoo wor varry short-seeted. In a few minnits at after ther wor an explosion 'at saanded like a cannon. Th'watter flew i' all directions an' th' set-pot lid flew aght o'th'winda. A'a! but shoo wor scared. Shoo didn't knaw what to do, but shoo hunted all raand an' square for th'puddin, an' when shoo couldn't finnd it, shoo wor fair heartslufted.

Abaat nooin, th'lads coom in looking as sackless as yo pleeas.

'Nah, mother,' they said. 'Is th'puddin ready?'

'Nay,' shoo said. 'Ther's noa puddin. It's towt me a lesson has this. Aw'll nivver cook o'th'Sunday ageean. It's dule hissen 'at's fotched it.' An' shoo tell'd 'em as weel as shoo could what had happened. They all reckoned to hunt for it, an' one on 'em fotched it throo th'naybour's an' put it i'th'set-pot ageean.

'Why, th'puddin's here, mother!' they said. 'Yo must ha' been dreeamin.'

71

'Aw've nooan ben dreeamin,' shoo said, 'but if th'dule hasn't had owt to do wi'it, some of his imps have!'

Soa they'd a reight gooid dinner, an' monny a laugh at after abaat th'boiled fooitball.

# 'Rambling Remarks – January'
## (from the 'Clock Almanack' of 1900.)

(The growing awareness of what killer diseases, such as tuberculosis, were all about is reflected in this essay in which Hartley grimly makes fun of what was a common disease in urban Yorkshire, killing thousands each year until the discovery of anti-biotics. Mike Robes (microbes), Back Silly (baccillae), Tube Harry Colosus (tuberculosis) and Hen Flewinsa (influenza) are Hartley's attempts to make light of these deadly illnesses through parody)

"A thing 'at's weel begun is hawf done" is an owd saying, but like a lot more sichlike, it isn't alus true. Aw've knawn lot's o'things 'at's had a gooid beginnin 'at's nivver getten ony farther; but aw hooap that willn't be th'cse wi' this year's 'Clock'. Yet what wi' Mike Robes, Back Silly, Tube Harry Colosus, Hen Flewinsa, Income Tax, Dog Licence, an' one trouble an' another, it's hard to feel safe abaat owt but th'rent-day an' deeath. He's a risky chap 'at's willin to lig odds on owt else nah days, tho' aw do believe ther's some fowk 'at's soa fond o'bettin 'at they'd leever have a wager on if they knew they'd loise, nor nivver bet at all.

It seems to be a age o' gamblin this an' it isn't confined to horse-racin an' card laikin. Churches an' chapels foster it as weel as public haases, an' a gooid deeal o'brass changed hands i'th'way o'trade 'at's nobbut thinly veneered wi' sich names as sharebrokin an' speculation. They mayn't be cards 'at they shuffle an' cut, but they can shuffle an' cut too when it suits ther purposes. Owd Barker 'at lives i' Cowling willn't even shuffle off this mortal coil for fear o' bein charged wi' gammin. Some of his poor relations wish he wod.

It's a uncertain world is this. Yo study an' plan an' skeeam befoor yo set th'ball rollin, but wheear it'll roll to, or ha far it'll goa is just a toss-up. When aw set this almanac arollin, thirty four years sin, aw little thowt it owd be runnin yet, an' aw'm thankful to all them 'at's gi'en it a kindly shove.

73

It's had it's obstacles to face, but it's baanced ovver 'em an' run faster an' faster a' farther nor before. Ther mayn't be mich in it, but ther's a gradely bit made aght on it.

'Aw reckon tha thinks thisen a bit of a poet,' a chap said to me t'other day, as aw wor suppin mi penny gill to swill daan some free lunch.

'Aye,' aw said. 'Aw do.'

'That's reight,' he said, 'but dooan't fancy 'at onnybody'll mistak thi for a Tennyson, for if tha does tha'll be sukt.'

'They'd be more likely to mistak him for Tennyson Smith,' said another, 'for they booath curl ther hair i'th'same fashion.'

Aw'm able to stand a gooid bit, but that wor just a little bit too thick, soa aw walked reight aght an' said nowt. I' less nor ten minnits aw wor in a barber's shop. Aw've sins enuff to answer for withaat addin to 'em, an' when that barber had done wi' me aw wor more likely to be taken for Bill Sykes nor Ted Smith.

Someha, this reminds me of a chap at Bradforth they called Baylee. He wor a gurt teetotaller an' he'd browt his wife an' childer up to th' same belief. He used to spaat a gooid deeal at Bands o' Hope meetins, an' tho' his subject wor wattery, he put soa mich spirit into it wol he fell sick an' had to send for th' doctor.

'You require a stimulant,' sed th' doctor. 'Take a little whiskey sometimes.'

'Me..me..me tak whiskey! What wod my flock think?' sed Baylee.

'They need not know. I can send it in a medicine bottle. You can ask for your shaving water and then mix a little and drink it hot,' said th'doctor.

Th'physic bottle coom all reight, an' next morning when th'doctor called Mrs Baylee wor in a sad way. 'It's his heead, doctor,' shoo sed. 'He's wrang in his heead! He's called for five lots o' shavin watter this morning an' when aw took th'last up, he wor dancing a hornpipe i'th'front o'th'glass!'

Baylee gate better, but he's left th'Band o'Hope.

When a chap desires to be famous, an' he's nawther hansom nor clivver nor rich, he's still one chonce, that is to be a bigger fooil nor onnybody else. He'll be as mich tawked abaat an' as mich written abaat as if he wor a member o' parliment, an' he'll even finnd fowk to envy an' imitate him. He willn't need to dress up for it, becoss a chap can be just as big a fooil in a parson's suit as he can if he's donned like a claan in a circus.

Th' mistak at fowk are apt to make is tryin to be a fooil asteead o' bein natteral. Ther's lots o' fooils – big fooils, too – who haven't leeast bit of a nooation ha clivver they are i' that line o' business. Of cooarse, th'biggest fooil will allus be th'chap 'at laffs at ivverbody's folly an' can't see his awn. Ther's monny a wed chap thinks he's fooilin his wife, when he's nobbut convincin her what a fooil shoo has for a husband. Noa gooid woman likes to hear her husband called a fooil, but ther's varry few 'at dooan't believe he is one.

If doin fooilish things shows a chap to be a fooil, why, ther's few young fowk 'at aren't fooilish; but ther's a chonce 'at they may turn aght wise as they grow owder. But ther's noa proof 'at they aren't fooils becoss they're owder. We can laff at a young fooil, but an owd fooil fills us wi' sorrow or contempt.

One o'th'warst sooarts o' fooils to deeal wi' is him 'at fancies 'at all th'world is leagued together to keep him daan soa as to help thersen up. Bless mi life! If he didn't exist at all, th'world wod nivver know th'difference. 'Ivvery dog has his day except me,' he says, when th'fact o'th'matter is he's had his chonces th'same as th'best on us, but he wor too lazy or too faint-hearted to seize 'em when they came. Ivverybody connot be lucky ivvery day, but onnybody may be lucky someday.

A chap 'at tries to get along honestly will varry likely succeed; but a chap 'at's detarmined to get on honestly or net is sewer to succeed, but aw dooan't call that bein lucky. Sharppractice may win wealth but it can nivver bring happiness an' content. This is a free country – too free, aw think, sometimes. Ther's moor fowk study th'laws o' this land to be able to evade 'em nor study 'em to be able to obey 'em.

Well, it's better to be a poor fooil nor a rich knave. Ther'll come a time when a chap's bankin acaant willn't amaant to owt. Yo connot pay extra for 'early doors' or book a seeat in advance i'th' world to come, noa matter ha rich yo are, for gowd an' lands willn't pass yo in. An' aw dooan't think ' at a chap 'at's lived a lazy useless life an' dees i'th'warkus will be able to get a front seeat awther bi pleadin poverty.

# 'Chaitin a Lanlord'
## (from the 'Clock Almanack' of 1909.)

Yo've yor job set if yo start o' tryin to chait a lanlord. Aw dooan't say 'at sich a thing nivver wor done, by onny meeans, but aw will say 'at a scooar tries on it an' fails, for one 'at succeeds. Th' fact is, as a rule, lanlords are soa mich accustomed to chattin other fowk to get ta'en in thersens.

Aw remember when aw wor a young chap gooin cooartin a lass 'at lived at a public haase – shoo wor a varry nice lass, an' aw put a deeal o' time in of a neet, an' monny a time when they wor a bit thrang, th'lanlord used to say, "Aw wish yo'd just wait on for hawf an haar, wol we get th'push ower." An' as it gave me moor chonces o' whisperin to Elizabeth Ann i'th'bar, an' squeezing her hand when shoo wor workin th' beer pump, aw used to help reg'lar away. Soa aw gate to be lukked on as one o'th'reg'lar sarvants after a bit, an' aw often used to stop in after closin time an' have a bit o'supper. Aw've oft seen 'at when summat had gooan wrang 'at put th'lanlord aght a but durin th'evenin, he used to goa wi' a bit o' chalk to th'back o'th'bar door, wheear he kept a list o' fowk 'at owed him owt for ale, an' he'd put daan an extra quart a piece all raand, just to soothe his temper a bit.

But aw'll tell yo a bit of a tale aw've heeard, abaat a chap 'at took a lanlord in reight weel. He wor called Bob Bentley, an' he wor a chap 'at wor varry fond o' doin bits o' conjurin tricks, makin hawpnys disappear up his coit-sleeves, an' sich like. One neet Bob went to a grand entertainment at th' Bradforth Mechanics' Institute, to see Professor Sharp, th'gurt ventriloquist an' conjuror. He'd nivver heeard o' ventriloquism befoor, an' he wor fare capt ha th'saand seemed to coom throo under th'flooar an' aght o'th'centre gasleet, an' aw dooan't knaw wheear beside.

"Ther's sombdy hidden up i'th'ceilin," he sed to a chap 'at wor sittin near him.

"Nowt at sooart," t'chap replied. "He does it all bi hissen."

"But ha does he do it?" Bob axed.

"It's ventriloquism," sed th'chap.

Bob wor varry unbelievin, but he went hooam that neet fair dumbfaanded at th'things he'd seen an' heeard. He axed several of his mates abaat it, but nubdy could tell him ha ventriloquism wor done, till one day when he wor gooan up to th'station to see abaat a trip ther wor to Morcambe, he happened to nooatice on th'bookstall a little sixpenny book entitled, "How to become a ventriloquist." He bowt it straight off, took it hooam, an' spent nearly all th'neet reading it an' practin th'art.

It wor slow wark at th'fust, but after a bit he began to do it better. He'd monny a rare bit o' fun at hooam wi' his missus, sendin her to th'door to get th'milk, when th'milkman hadn't coom; an' he'd have her runnin upstairs to th'childer, when they wor all fast asleep i' bed. At last th'poor woman began o' thinkin 'at th'haase wor haunted, soa he telled her abaat it an' shoo wor rare an' sewted. They'd plenty o' larks wi' ther naybours, makkin 'em believe 'at sumbdy wor bein smoar'd i'th'chimla, an' freetenin 'em aght o' ther wits.

At last shoo sed, "Bob, nah 'at th'childer are growin up a bit, aw've soa mich sewin an' mendin to do 'at tha reely mun buy me a sewin machine."

"Aw'll get thi one tomorn, lass, if tha'll finnd th'brass," he sed.

"Aw can get one misen if aw've th'brass, lumpheead!" shoo replied.

"Well, aw've noan, an' aw dooan't knaw wheear it's to coom throo," he sed.

"Can't ta gi' a performance o' ventriloquism at th'Mechanics' Institute?" shoo sed.

This set Bob a-thinkin, an' after a day or two's cudgelin of his brains, he hit on a plan.

It wor abaat th'middle o' December at th'time an' a chap 'at lived next dooar 'at kept a dog had been sayin 'at he wor baan to draand it at th'yeear-end, for he worn't baan to pay three hawf-craans ageeean for it licence. Soa Bob went in an' begged th'dog, promisin him I should have a gooid hooam.

He an' his wife an' childer made a deeal o' fuss o' th'animal durin th'few days it stopped wi' 'em. Bob allus had it sittin on a chair near to him at meeal times an' he used to feed it theear. Th' dog gat soa used to it, 'at th'moment he sat daan to th' table, th'dog knew 'at some jock wor stirrin an' it jumped up on to th'chair an' sat waitin to be fed, as intelligent as a Christian.

At last Bob thowt all wor ready for his plan, soa he set off wi'th' dog to a public haase he knew, net soa far throo Lister's Mill at Manningham. Nah th'lanlord o' this haase had once paid Bob a bad coin o' some kind, an' refused to tak it back. It wor two or three yeear ago, an' noa daat th'lanlord had forgetten all abaat it; but Bob hadn't. He wor detarmined to mak this chap pay for his wife's new sewin machine. When he gate to th'haase, he marched in wi' th'dog at his heels an' went into a room theear wheear a deeal o'Lister's hands gooas ta get ther drinkins. Th'room wor empty at th'time soa Bob sat daan at a table an' rang th' bell. In coom th'lanlord in a minnit. "Can aw have summat to ait?" axed Bob.

"Dinner's ovver nah," sed th'lanlord, "but aw can get yo sumat, aw've noa daat. Ha wod a mutton chop an' some mashed potates sewt yo?"

"Fust rate," sed Bob. "Bring me a plate."

"An' bring me a plate o'th'same," sed th'dog.

Th'lanlord stared wol his een nearly dropt aght of his heead. Th' dog wor sittin on a chair wi' his heead on one side an' lookin as wise as owt.

"Aw thowt aw heeard th'dog ax for a plate, too," sed th'lanlord.

"Tha did," answered Bob. "They aren't common, but that one connot only tawk, it can understand all 'at's sed to it."

Th'landlord wor rayther afraid, but he went an' ordered th'chops. Just as he gate to th'door, Bob called aght, "Bring me a pint o' ale wol th'chops are cookin."

"An' bring me a pint, too," sed th'dog. "Aw'm as dry as a dust-cart."

Th'lanlord browt th'ale an' set one pot i'front o' Bob an' th'other for th'dog. Then he went aght ageean to fetch his wife in to see th'tawkin dog. As sooin as he'd gooan, Bob drank off th'dog's pint an' set th'empty pot daan ageean i'th'same place. In a bit th'lanlord an' th'lanlady booath coom in an' shoo sed, "Aw dooan't think it can tawk at all. Yor only gammonin me."

"It can sup ale at onnyrate," sed th'lanlord, lookin at th'empty pot.

"Aw can soa," sed th'dog, "an' it's reight gooid ale, too!"

Well, booath th'lanlord an' his wife wor fait capt. Th'dog answered several questions th'missus put it to it just as weel as if it had been to a Board Schooil an' had passed th'fourth standard. Shoo wor soa sewted wi' it 'at when th'chops coom, shoo cut th'dog's up into bits an' mixed it wi' th' potatoes. Th'dog thanked her for her kindness an' axed her to put noa pepper on it.

Wol they wor aitin, th'lanlady took her husband up to t'other end o'th'raam an' sed, "Yo wor sayin t'other day 'at th'custom wod sewer to drop off as sooin as th'Pantomime started at th'theatre. Nah if we hed that dog i'th'haase, norther Pantomimes nor owt else wod keep fowk away. Why, th'haase wod be craaded ivvery neet! All Bradforth would coom to see it, an' we could mak whativver it costs ovver an' ovver ageean. Besides, when fowk's sewted an' have summat to entertain 'em, they aren't soa partic'lar abaat th'quality o' ther drinks, an' we could let daan th'whisky an' gin as mich ageean as we do, an' all that wod be clear profit."

He knew 'at shoo wor reight i' what shoo sed, an' that th'tawkin dog wod be th'best draw 'at had ivver been seen in a public haase. Soa he went back to Bob an' sed, "My missus has ta'en quite a fancy to yor dog. Have yo a mind to sell it?"

"Aw dooan't think aw can pairt wi' it. Tho' to tell yo th'truth, a bit o' brass wod coom in varry handy at awr haase just at present; for what wi' th'rent an' doctorin an' one thing an' another, aw'm abaat cleeaned aght. Still, aw dooan't like to pairt wi'th'dog."

"Aw should think net!" sed th'animal. "Aw'm nooan baan to pairt wi' yo onnyway!"

"Just hear that!" sed th'lanlady. "It's as sensible as a child."

"Of cooarse aw am," th'dog replied, an' this pleeased 'em more nor ivver. Nowt wod sewt 'em but he mud state a price for it.

"Aw willn't be selled, soa that's flat!" sed th'dog.

"Aw'll give yo five-paand daan," sed th'lanlord.

"Five-paand!" sed th'dog. "Five paand! What's five paand, aw should like to knaw? Aw'm worth twenty paands of onnybody's brass."

"Just hearken to it," sed th'lanlady. "We must yo, yo sensible doggie." An' shoo patted him on th'heead an' it wagged it tail an' tried to lick her face. Bob an' th'lanlord argued for a gooid bit, th'dog puttin a word in nah an' then, an' at last Bob agreed to tak ten paands, brass daan.

Th'lanlord went an' fotched th'brass, an' when Bob had getten it safely in his pocket, th'dog sed, "Yo aren't really baan to sell me, are yo?"

"Aw am," sed Bob.

"But aw willn't be selled," sed th'dog. "Aw'm nooan baan to be made a public haase show at my time o' life!"

"Yo'll have a varry gooid hooam," sed Bob.

"Yo shall that!" th'lanlady answered. "Plenty o'th'varry best booath to ait an' sup, an' a nice warm bed to sleep in of a neet."

"Aw've a warm bed at hooam, an' aw've nivver been clammed yet. Noa, aw'll stop at th'owd shop."

"Get a bit o' band an' tee him up wi' his collar, till aw've getten clean away, an' then he'll sattle daan aw've noa daat, an' be as happy as owt," sed Bob.

"Aw willn't," sed th'dog.

Soa th'lanlord gate some string an' tied th'dog to a table-leg, an' Bob gate up to goa away. "What do yo call him?" sed th'lanlady.

"Charley wor his name once, but latterly we've called him th' Grand Owd Man, becoss he's sich a beggar for tawkin," sed Bob, who patted him on th'heead. "Gooid-bye, owd lad. Aw'll coom an' see thi sometimes to see hah tha'rt getting on."

"An' are yo pairtin wi' me?" axed th'dog.

"Aw am for sewer," replied Bob.

"What for ?" sed th'dog. "What hev aw done 'at aw didn't owt to hev done?"

"Nowt at all. But tha tawks soa mich," sed Bob.

"Then if that's th'case," sed th'dog, "an' yo're pairtin wi' me for noa other reason, aw'll tak mi solemn davy at aw'll nivver spaik another word ageean!"

An' it nivver did.

## 'RAMBLING REMARKS – JANUARY'
### (FROM THE 'CLOCK ALMANACK' OF 1911.)

Another time we start aght for a year's ramblin. It's to be hooaped we shalln't get lost. We've come varry near it a time or two, but we've managed to land safely up to nah, an' we mun trust to luck. When one tries for summat an' fails he looks on it as a misfortun, but he's apt to forget 'at misfortuns are often blessins in disguise. A sensible chap knaws 'at misfortuns, like other things, have a best side as weel as a worst. Aw've made it a rule for a deeal o' yeears to allus mak th'best o'th'best an' nivver to mak bad worse wi' freeatin abaght it. That's why it is aw've been able to goa through life wi' more pleasure an' less pain nor mooast fowk. Ther's nowt like a bit o' filosofy for smoothin things ovver, an' yo'll finnd it varry useful sometimes. If yo think sometimes 'at yo've a deeal more worries nor yo have pleasures, just get a cleean slate an' a bit o' pencil an' write daan all yer troubles on one side, an' then turn it over an' write all yor blessings on t'other. Yo'll sooin see 'at yo've more to be thankful for nor what yo have to grummel abaat. Dooan't think abaaat ha monny troubles yo've had, but abaat ha monny yo've missed.

Washington Irving says, 'Little minds are tamed and subdued by misfortune; but great minds rise above it.' Soa, have a great mind. If all th'troubles o' mankind wor heeaped up in a lump, an' then equally shared ght amang us all, them 'at think thersen mooast put on an' miserable wod be glad to have ther owd troubles back ageean asteead o'th'new uns they'd getten. If yo railly have a trouble, dooan't brood ovver it; an' whativver else yo do, dooan't tawk abaat it.

> "laugh and the world laughs with you;
> Weep and you weep alone;
> For the sad old earth must borrow its mirth,
> It has troubles enough of its own.

Be glad, and your friends are many;
Be sad, and you lose them all;
There are none to decline your nectared wine,
But alone you must drink life's gall."

It's as natteral for pain to follow pleasure as it is for neet to follow day. If it worn't soa, life wod be soa dull 'at we should all dee i'th'dumps. What does Edwin Waugh say abaat it?

"If mon had been made for a bit ov a spree,
An' th'world wor a marlockin schoo,
Wi' nowt nobbut heytin, an' drinkin, an' glee,
An' haliday gam to go throo,
He'd sicken afore his frolic wor o'er
An' feel he'd been born for a foo."

We worn't all born to be fooils, aw dooan't think, but we mooastly manage to come varry near it. When aw've been i' onny trouble, if aw've taken misen seriously to think abaat it, aw've come to th' conclusion 'at it's nobbut what aw've been seekin, an' varry oft what aw've bowt an' paid for. Well, experience is a grand schooil. It may cost a lot, but it's th'only way mooast on us gain sense. We're a dissatisfied lot, takkin us all together. If a chap breaks one leg, he's sewer to say, 'Aw wodn't ha' cared soa mich if it had been t'other.' If he knaws two young lasses an' weds one, it willn't be a month befoor he'll say, 'If aw'd to wed ageean, aw should do different.'

If a chap works hard till he's owd, an' manages to save a bit a brass, he'll caant it over an' say, 'What's th'use on it to me. Aw'm too owd to enjoy it.' An' if he's spent all as fast as he gate it, when owd age comes and finnds him a pauper, he'll whine, 'If aw'd mi time to do ageean, aw'd live it different.' But ten to one he wodn't. Soa what's it matter.

## 'Rambling Remarks – October'
### (from the 'Clock Almanack' of 1914.)

We've getten to th'fag-end o'th'year nah, an' we munn't expect mich more fine weather for a bit. Sometimes we're favoured wi' a bit o' sunshine an' it's varry welcome when it does come, but we dooan't expect it. Young chaps put ther bats an' balls away for another season, an' lasses gooidbye to ther hoakey sticks. Fooitball reigns for th' next six months an' young an' owd look to ther muscles an' begin trainin. Aw can enjoy watchin a game o' fooitball, tho' aw dooan't knaw mich abaat it, for they dooan't laik at it as we used to do when aw wor a lad. Aw connot help thinkin sometimes 'at if they'd to train as mich an' work as hard for summat better, they might do more gooid i'th'world an' benefit thersen more. Of course, my opinions dooan't caant for mich nah days as aw belong to a generation 'at's passin away.

Well, things change, an' if aw can't change wi' 'em, aw mun be content to stand to one side. Th'young uns have a reight to ther innins an' aw hooap they'll enjoy 'em. If aw tried to laik fooitball nah, aw should look a bigger fooil nor aw am, an' that's needless.

Horse-racin, bettin an' card-laikin used to be called gamlin, but nah it's 'specilation', or if yo belang to th'upper ten it's 'investment.' Well it may be all reight, but aw'm like th'Scotchman – 'aw hae mi doots.' Shakespeare says, 'A rose by any other name will smell as sweet' an' that's true enough. A stink will be just as sickenin if yo call it perfume. Ther's a deeal o' things tolerated at this day 'at we should shun if we gav 'em ther reight names. It strikes me 'at we're gettin too polite to be truthful in this day.

If a gentleman has been havin a gooid time an' is seen to stagger a bit, he's 'slightly elevated,' an' a kindly poleeceman taks him hooam; but if he's a poor workin man, they run him in for bein drunk an he's fined 2s 6d an' costs. Reight enough, it's all according to law, but what abaat justice? It's th'owd tale ageean. One man may stail a horse an' goa scot free, an' another will be sent to quad for lookin ovver a hedge at one.

Ther wor a time when we sent men to parliament to represent us an' to mak gooid laws for us. They thowt it an honour to goa for sich purposes, but what do they goa for nah? Four hundred a year an' cheeap dinners an' drinks. Aw dooan't meean to say 'at ther's noa gooid men i' parliment – soa ther is i' Wakefield Prison – but they're in a minority.

Haivver, what can't be cured mun be endured; yet ther's a limit comes to endurance sometimes, an' aw think we're drawin near th'end.

Ther's allus a lot o'tawk abaat reform, but ther's nobbut one way to get it, an' that way is to let ivvery man reform hissen, an' we shall sooin have a better world. Aw think aw happen connot do better nor act on that motto missen, soa as aw've rambled on in a fault-finndin strain soa long, aw'll shut up, or aw may offend somdy, an' aw connot afford, an' dooan't want to mak enemies.

We should all be prepared for trouble when it comes. A day may look breet an' cleear, but it's allus advisable to have yor umbrella ready, yet ther's noa need to put it up before it rains.

It's better to hooap tho' th'claads hang low,
An' to keep yor een uplifted;
For th'breet blue sky will sooin peep through,
When th'dark black claads are rifted.
Ther wor nivver a neet withaat a mornin,
Nor an evenin withaat a day,
An' th'darkest haar 'at ivver comes
Is th'haar before the dawnin.

# THE PREFACE FROM THE
## 'CLOCK ALMANACK' OF 1915.

(This was the last number published during John Hartley's lifetime for he died in December of that year. The almanac for 1916 was edited by him, but published posthumously.)

Forty-nine year old today! Bless mi life! Ha time does keep joggin on. Next year will be my Jubilee! Who could ha thowt it? An' still, when aw luk back it nobbut seeams like t'other day. Well, i' all th' years aw've spent tryin to pleeas yo, aw haven't had things all straight forrard an' pleasant. Monny a time aw've met wi' disappointments an' want o' sympathy. Aw should ha' gi'en up i' despair if aw hadn't been cheered wi' kind words aw've had sent to me, bi them 'at's lukt ovver mi faults an' failins, an' confessed they'd fun summat to pleeas 'em. Soa aw've buckled to ageean, cried 'nil desperandum' an' hooapt for better things.

> All the lessons of the time
>     Teach us fair,
> 'Tis a blunder and a crime
>     To despair.
> When we Suffer, 'tis to bless
> Other moments with success;
> From our losses we may trace
> Something better in their place;
> Everything in earth and sky
>     Seems to shout,
>     'Don't give up until you die –
>       Fight it out!'

An' soa yo see aw'm still wrestling wi' it. Owd age keeps creepin on, an' mi pen doesn't run as swiftly, nor mi thowts flow as freely as they did i' years gooan by. But aw keep a stiff upper lip, an' aw've noa intention o' throwin up th' sponge until aw'm licked – an' that isn't yet! It's a grand thing to live an' grow owd. Aw dooan't think onny young fowk ivver knaw what a grand an' lovely world this is, as a chap 'at's lived in it long enuff to prove it. Aw think aw knaw summat abaght it, becoss aw've experienced it. It doesn't need a chap to be a worldly chap to be a lover o'th'world. One meets wi' lots o' things i'th'journey throo this life 'at gets his back up, but that's becoss he doesn't stop to think. If yo're disheartened an' despairin, just goa aght into th'world wi' a mind ready to tak things as yo finnd 'em, an' be determined to mak th' best o' things an' yo'll sooin be able to come back an' be willin to admit things are better ner yo expected to finnd 'em.

Ther's poverty an' sufferin goa whear yo will, but ther's smilin faces, kind hearts, lovin words an' liberal hands, ivverywhear. If ivver aw've fun misen in a tight corner, an' could see noa way aght, ther's allus some strong an' willin hand has dragged me aght o' darkness into sunshine ageean. Aw'm noan weary o' this world, net aw, marry! Tho' aw've had a gooid share on it. Aw've sense enuff to knaw this world is all reight if fowk'll nobbut use it reight, an' when aw hear fowk grummel abaat it, aw ax misen, 'What have yo ivver done to mak it better?' It's pure nonsense to say yo nivver had a chonce to do owt to mak it better. It isn't true. Have yo ivver desired to do it? Ther nivver wor a body livin, noa matter ha waik an' poor, who couldn't if he tried do summat to help his brothers an' sisters, if it wer nobbut to show thankfulness for what others did for him. Dooan't repine becoss yo see another better off ner yorsen. Remember it nobbut for a time. When deeath comes, we'st all be equal soa far as this world's riches are consarned, an' when futur blessins come to be shared aght, yo willn't be rewarded for what yo've done, but for what yo've tried to do. Ther's monny a man livin to-day who's considered a failure, who will get a reward he nivver hooaped for; an' monny a successful purse-praad man, when on earth, will be varry second-rate when th'grand distribution taks place.

Then what's th'gooid o' freeatin? Th'past is gooan, th' present will sooin be past, but th'futur, we may rest content, is all for th'best, for them 'at trust it an' desire to desarve it.

Well, it's abaat time aw stopped praichin. Aw dooan't get paid for that! My duty, as aw see it, is to cheer fowk up a bit. Tell 'em things to mak 'em laff; change sad, glumpy faces into cheerful lukkin-glasses, whear others can see reflections of happiness an' can be induced to smile, too. Providence, aw'm sewer, intended 'at we shouldn't be unhappy, or else we shouldn't be surraanded wi' blue skies an' glorious sunsets, an' awr walks made beautiful wi' wild flaars. That man 'at praiches gloomy sarmons is a sinner! He meeans weel, but he's made a mistak. Ther's few men have been made better becoss o' th'fear of hell; but thaasands have been saved bi th' glories o' heaven. Ther's monny think aw should be doin more gooid i' this world if aw treated things more seriously. Well, that may be true, but aw connot. It isn't my line. Aw just have to write as aw think, an' if aw connot see things in th'same way as others do, that's mi misfortune an' net mi fault.

"Smile a little, smile a little,
Sing a happy song;
Life is full of thorny places
And the road seems long;
Smile a little, smile a little,
Make someone feel glad;
Earth is full of stony places,
And some heart is sad."

Hooap is a grand thing. If man had been born withaat hooap, he wodn't want to live. Sorrow's antidooat is Hooap.

"Mid the turmoil and the clamour
I hear Hope singing still –
The mists may cloud the meadow,
But the sunlight crowns the hill.'"

89

Well, then, let's all indulge i' Hooap. Ther's a better time comin; have a bit more patience. Ther wor nivver a man born into this world to be miserable. Ther's plenty who are soa, more's the pity. Then let me try, as far as lays i' mi paar, to mak a few happy. A woman sent me a letter t'other day sayin my Almanack had saved her husband's life. It seems he'd been poorly for a long time an' wor daan i'th'dumps. Shoo read him a tale aght o'th' "Clock" an' it tickled his fancy. This caused him to read th' remainder, an' after axin for his supper, he gate it an' went to sleep. Next mornin he felt better, an' in a few days wor able to get up an' goa to his wark. This cheered me up a bit. Aw wish somdy wod write a almanack 'at wod have th'same effect o' me – but unfortunately aw nivver liked wark!

God bless yo all! That's th'sincere prayer of

JOHN HARTLEY.

# A NOTE ON HARTLEY'S
# DIALECT SPELLING AND
# VOCABULARY

# A NOTE ON HARTLEY'S DIALECT SPELLING.

The thorny subject of dialect spelling constantly crops up when one is editing dialect-writing. There is no standard way of spelling in dialect as there is in the standard language, precisely because dialect is dialect and words vary in pronunciation from region to region. The spelling of standard English is not phonetic, as we all know to our cost when young; but dialect spelling is phonetic largely, that is, the writer is trying to represent by standard alphabetical letters the sounds of the words he is using, but he sometimes misses the mark. (For example, John Hartley uses the spelling "mait" for "meat" where I would have used "meyt" – there is a diphthong here in which the "e" is open and the "i" is closed.) Moreover, John Hartley gives variant spellings throughout his works, sometimes in the same piece; for example, "wheear" and "whear" for "where".

The spelling is further complicated because Hartley was brought up in Halifax, but lived in a variety of places in the West Riding, such as Leeds and Bradford, where the pronunciation is slightly different from Halifax. The whole of this region is a "buffer" zone between the true northern dialects of the East and North Ridings and the northern dales of the West Riding, and the north-midland dialect of the industrial West Riding; so we find in Hartley's works a northern form of a word sometimes e.g. "thrang" meaning "busy", sometimes its north-midland form "throng" (Old Joseph displays the same inconsistency in "Wuthering Heights"; which is not surprising, as Haworth is only eight or so miles from Halifax.). This peculiarity of the dialect around Halifax may also account for pluralities such as "o'er", "ower" and "ovver" for "over"; and "wor", "wur" and "wer" for "were".

Hartley also varies the definite article spelling from "th'", which is the common pronunciation along the Lancashire border and in East Lancashire itself, to "t'" which is the more usual form of "the" in West Yorkshire (In many Yorkshire towns "the" is omitted together and replaced with a glottal stop.). Bearing all this in mind, I hope the readers of Hartley's work will understand – and tolerate – his orthography more. As a rider, I must confess to some alteration of his punctuation, which is at times a little bizarre, probably because many of his works were never proof-read but went straight to print, warts and all.

# VOCABULARY.

### A.

| | | |
|---|---|---|
| Aat, aght, aht | = | Out |
| Abaat, abaght, abaht | = | About |
| Aboon | = | Above |
| Afoor, afore | = | Before |
| Agean, ageean | = | Again |
| Aitin | = | Eating |
| Allus | = | Always |
| Anent | = | Next to |
| Antidooat | = | Antidote |
| Araand | = | Around |
| Asteead | = | Instead |
| At after | = | Afterwards |
| 'at's | = | That's |
| Aw | = | I |
| Aw'd | = | I had |
| Awr | = | Our |
| Aw'st, awst | = | I shall, I should |
| Axin | = | Asking |

### B.

| | | |
|---|---|---|
| Baan | = | Going |
| Baat, baght | = | Without |
| Bairn | = | Child |
| Band | = | String |
| Bate | = | Bit (verb) |
| To beg on | = | To ask for work at a mill or factory |
| Belangin | = | Belonging |
| Bethowt | = | i.) Remembered ii.) Decided |
| Th'betterness | = | The superior quality of |
| Big haase | = | Work-house, Poor house |

| | | |
|---|---|---|
| Bin | = | Been |
| Blinnd | = | Blind |
| A bob | = | A shilling (5 new pence) |
| Boggards | = | Evil, ghostly creatures |
| Booath | = | Both |
| Booits | = | Boots |
| Bowt | = | Bought |
| Brace buttons | = | Trouser buttons (for braces) |
| Braik | = | Break |
| Brass | = | Money |
| Brat | = | Apron |
| Breead | = | Bread |
| Breetened | = | Brightened |
| Breetest | = | Brightest |
| Brokken | = | Broken |
| Browt | = | Brought |
| Bum-bailey | = | Bumbailiff |
| To buttle | = | To share out |

## C.

| | | |
|---|---|---|
| Caanty | = | County |
| Caared on | = | Sat on |
| Capped, capt | = | Surprised |
| Chaitin | = | Cheating |
| Chaymer | = | Bedroom |
| Cheeap | = | Cheap |
| Childer | = | Children |
| Chimla, chimley | = | Chimney |
| Chine | = | Back-bone |
| Choose ha | = | Choose (think) how you will |
| Clammed | = | Hungry |
| Claat | = | Clout (patch) |
| Cloise | = | Close |
| Cluff | = | Clough (an escarpment) |

| | | |
|---|---|---|
| Coit-laps | = | Coat-tails |
| Consait | = | Conceit |
| Consarn | = | Concern |
| Coom | = | Come |
| Cowd | = | Cold |
| Craad | = | Crowd |
| Craan | = | Crown |
| Craytur | = | Creature |
| Cun, curran | = | Currant |

D.

| | | |
|---|---|---|
| Daan, dahn | = | Down |
| Daan th'yard | = | A euphemism for going to the toilet |
| Dar | = | Dare |
| Davy | = | Oath (affidavit) |
| Deeaf | = | Deaf |
| Deeal | = | Deal (very) |
| Deein | = | Dying |
| Desarves | = | Deserves |
| Donced | = | Danced |
| Donned | = | Dressed |
| Dooan't, dunnot | = | Don't |
| Doy | = | Little one (a term of endearment for a child) |
| Dreely | = | Persistently |
| Drinkins | = | Mid-morning or mid-day refreshments |
| Drinkin time | = | Mid-morning break |
| Druffen | = | Drunken |
| Dule | = | Devil |

E.

| | | |
|---|---|---|
| E'en, een | = | Eyes |
| Etten | = | Eaten |
| Eyt | = | Eat |

# F.

| | | |
|---|---|---|
| Faand | = | Found |
| Faantains | = | Fountains |
| Factry | = | Factory |
| Fair-, fare-, -capt | = | Very surprised |
| Fain | = | Eager, enthusiastic |
| Fan, fun | = | Found |
| Faw'n | = | Fallen |
| Fear'd, flayd | = | Afraid |
| Fellies | = | Fellows |
| Finnd | = | Find |
| Fit | = | Feet |
| Fizenomony | = | Physiognomy |
| Flaars | = | Flowers |
| Flags, flagstooans | = | Pavement stones |
| Flaysome | = | Painful |
| Fly at | = | Angrily quarrel with |
| Foir | = | Fire |
| Fooiled | = | Fooled |
| Fooit | = | Foot |
| Forrard | = | Forward |
| Fotch | = | Fetch |
| Fowk | = | Folk |
| Fratch | = | Quarrel |
| Freeatin | = | Fretting, worrying |
| Freetenin | = | Frightening |
| Fresh | = | Slightly intoxicated |
| Fust | = | First |

# G.

| | | |
|---|---|---|
| Gaan | = | Gown |
| Gab | = | Senseless chatter |
| Gam | = | Game |
| Gammin | = | Gambling |
| Gammonin | = | Tricking |

| | | |
|---|---|---|
| Gat, gate | = | Got |
| Getherin | = | i.) A gathering  ii.) a boil |
| Getten | = | Got |
| Gi' | = | Give |
| Gill | = | Half a pint (of beer – pronounced 'jill') |
| Gloored o'er | = | Looked over intently |
| Goa | = | Go |
| Goan, gooan | = | Gone |
| Gooid | = | Good |
| Gowd | = | Gold |
| Gradely | = | Healthy, well, pleasing |
| Grummeled | = | Grumbled |
| Gurt | = | Great |

H.

| | | |
|---|---|---|
| Ha, haa | = | How |
| Ha' | = | Have |
| Haar | = | Hour |
| Haase | = | House |
| Han'l | = | Handle |
| Hawf a craan | = | Half a crown (15 new pence) |
| Hawpny | = | Half-penny |
| Hawpoth | = | Half-penny worth |
| Heartslufted | = | Downcast, upset |
| Heead | = | Head |
| Heigh | = | High |
| Hev | = | Have |
| Hing | = | Hang |
| Hissel, hissen | = | Himself |
| Hoal | = | Whole |
| Hoam | = | Home |
| Hoap | = | Hope |
| Hoilful | = | Roomful |
| Howd | = | Hold |
| Huggin | = | Carrying |

## I.

| | | |
|---|---|---|
| Itsen | = | Itself |
| Ivver | = | Ever |
| Ivvery | = | Every |

## J.

| | | |
|---|---|---|
| Jamaka creeam | = | Rum |
| Jarkin | = | Jerking |
| Jawn | = | Jamb |
| Jerryhoil | = | A hidey hole (especially from the wife) |
| Jock | = | Food |

## K.

| | | |
|---|---|---|
| Knaw | = | Know |
| Kursmiss | = | Christmas |

## L.

| | | |
|---|---|---|
| Laikin | = | i.) Playing  ii.) out of work  iii.) idling |
| Lapt | = | Wrapped |
| Lat | = | Late |
| Leck on | = | Latch on (make contact with) |
| Leetnin | = | Lightning |
| Leet | = | Light |
| Leever | = | Rather, prefer |
| Lewkin | = | Looking |
| To lick | = | To beat, to win |
| Lig | = | Lie down |
| Loanly | = | Lonely |
| Lukkin-glass | = | Mirror |

# M.

| | | |
|---|---|---|
| Maase | = | Mouse |
| Maath | = | Mouth |
| Mail | = | Meal |
| Mait | = | Meat |
| Mak | = | Make |
| Makkin | = | Making |
| Mangle | = | Wringing-machine (used for squeezing excess water from clothes on washing day) |
| Net shoo marry! | = | Not she indeed! |
| Marlock | = | i.) Horseplay<br>ii.) a practical joke |
| Mewsic | = | Music |
| Mich | = | Much |
| Milns | = | Textile mills |
| Minit-, minnit | = | Minute |
| Misel, misen | = | Myself |
| Mission | = | A mission chapel |
| Mistak | = | Mistake |
| Mooar | = | More |
| Mooast | = | Most |
| Monny | = | Many |
| Mud, mun | = | Must, might |
| Mullock | = | A terrible mess |
| Munn't | = | Mustn't |

# N.

| | | |
|---|---|---|
| Naa, nah | = | Now |
| Natteral | = | Natural |
| Nawther | = | Neither |
| Naybour | = | Neighbour |
| Neer, nivver | = | Never |
| Neet | = | Night |
| Neive | = | Fist |

| | | |
|---|---|---|
| Ner, nor | = | Than |
| Net | = | Not |
| Noa | = | No |
| Noas, nooas | = | Nose |
| Noashun, nooation | = | Notion |
| Nobbut | = | Only |
| Nomony | = | Sermon, diatribe |
| Nooin | = | Noon |
| Nowt | = | Nothing |
| Nubdy | = | Nobody |
| Nur an' spell | = | Knurr and spell (a game played with a pick handle and a small ball) |

## O.

| | | |
|---|---|---|
| O'er, over, ower | = | Over |
| Ommost | = | Almost |
| On | = | Of (e.g. "two on us" = "two of us") |
| Ooinin | = | Depriving of food |
| Owd | = | Old |
| Th'owd lass | = | The wife |
| Ovver-topped | = | Excelled |

## P.

| | | |
|---|---|---|
| Paand | = | Pound |
| Paar | = | Power |
| Pairt | = | Part |
| Pairt-donned | = | Half-dressed |
| Paper o'spice | = | A bag of sweets |
| Paylor | = | Parlour |
| Peepies | = | Eyes (used with children) |
| Peggy-tub | = | Washing-tub |
| Pew | = | Pew-rent in church or chapel |
| Pictur | = | Picture |

| | | |
|---|---|---|
| Pinchin | = | i.) Scraping to save money   ii.) Stealing |
| Pinnin | = | Holding down |
| Gettin ther planets ruled | = | Having their destinies ruled by the stars |
| Pooark | = | Pork |
| Pooisen | = | Poison |
| Pool'd, pooled | = | Pulled |
| Potates | = | Potatoes |
| Praad | = | Proud |
| Practin | = | Practising |
| Praichin | = | Preaching |

## Q.

| | | |
|---|---|---|
| Quad | = | Prison |

## R.

| | | |
|---|---|---|
| Raainin | = | Raining |
| Raam | = | Room |
| Raand | = | Round |
| Raik | = | i.) Rake   ii.) reach |
| Ramellin | = | Rambling (in mind) |
| Rare an' sewted | = | Very pleased |
| To reckon | = | To pretend |
| Reet, reight | = | Right |
| Rhubub | = | Rhubarb |
| Rooad | = | Road |
| i' mi rooad | = | In my way |
| Rooasy | = | Rosy |

## S.

| | | |
|---|---|---|
| Saand | = | Sound |
| Sackless | = | Unconcerned, carefree |
| Sactackels | = | Lifts |
| Sam | = | Lift up |

| | | |
|---|---|---|
| Sarve | = | Serve |
| Scoors | = | Scores |
| Seet | = | Sight |
| Set-pot | = | A large metal container for boiling food or clothes in |
| Sewer | = | Sure |
| Shackle | = | Wrist |
| Shail on | = | To move cautiously and sluggishly, like a tide coming in |
| Shak | = | Shake |
| Shoolders | = | Shoulders |
| Th'shot | = | The bill |
| Sich | = | Such |
| To side | = | To clear away |
| Singel | = | Single, unmarried |
| Skeeam | = | Scheme |
| Smoar'd | = | Smothered |
| Smook | = | Smoke |
| Snawin | = | Snowing |
| Soa | = | So |
| Soil | = | Sole |
| Som'dy'd | = | Somebody had |
| Sooap | = | Soap |
| Spaat | = | Spout, talk a lot |
| Spaik, speeak | = | Speak |
| Spake | = | Spoke |
| Speklate | = | Speculate |
| Speykin | = | Speaking |
| Spice | = | Sweets |
| To square | = | To tidy up |
| Stail | = | Steal |
| Stalled | = | Tired, bored, out of patience |
| Stiver | = | A very small amount, nothing |
| Stoory | = | Storey |

| | | |
|---|---|---|
| Stooan | = | Stone |
| Studden | = | Stood (tolerated) |
| Sukt | = | Taken in, fooled |
| Summat | = | Something |
| Summin | = | Adding up accounts |
| Surelee | = | Surely |

## T.

| | | |
|---|---|---|
| Ta, tha | = | Thou |
| Taan | = | Town |
| Takken | = | Taken |
| Takken badly | = | Taken ill |
| Takker-in | = | Taker – in (superviser) |
| Teah | = | Tea |
| Tee | = | Tie |
| Telled | = | Told |
| Tewk | = | Took |
| Thaasand | = | Thousand |
| Thack | = | Roof |
| Thear, theear | = | There |
| Thease, theas | = | These |
| Them | = | Those |
| Ther | = | i.) They're ii.) their iii.) there |
| Thisen | = | Thyself |
| Thowt | = | Thought |
| Thrang, throng | = | Busy |
| Thro, throo | = | From |
| Thunner | = | Thunder |
| Tomorn | = | Tomorrow |
| Tooad | = | Toad |
| Trapesin | = | Walking slowly |
| Tummeld | = | Tumbled |
| Tuppince | = | Twopence |
| Tyke | = | i.) Rascal ii.)a Yorkshireman |

## U.

| | | |
|---|---|---|
| Un | = | One |
| Us | = | Our |
| Us sen | = | Ourselves |

## V.

| | | |
|---|---|---|
| Varry | = | Very |

## W.

| | | |
|---|---|---|
| War | = | Worse |
| Wark | = | i.) Work  ii.) ache |
| Warkhus | = | Workhouse |
| Watter | = | Water |
| Wayver, weyver | = | Weaver |
| Weel | = | Well |
| Weet | = | Wet |
| Wesh-haase | = | Wash-house |
| Weshin | = | Washing |
| We'st | = | We shall |
| Whear, wheear, wheer | = | Where |
| Whoal, whooal | = | Whole |
| Wick | = | i.) Week  ii.) alive with lice   iii.) lively |
| Winda | = | Window |
| Withaat | = | Without |
| Wodn't | = | Wouldn't |
| Wol | = | i.) While  ii.) until |
| Wolted | = | Lurched |
| Worn't | = | Wasn't |

## Y.

| | | |
|---|---|---|
| Yed | = | Head |
| Yeeast | = | Yeast |
| Yorsen | = | Yourself |

# BIBLIOGRAPHY

"John Hartley" by W. J. Halliday (1940) – Yorkshire Dialect Society Transactions.

"John Hartley" by J. H. Waddington (1939) – Halifax Courier Ltd.

"Notes on the West Riding Dialect Almanacs" by B. T. Dyson (1975) – Yorkshire Dialect Society Transactions.

"Yorkshire Dialect" by John Waddington-Feather (1970) – Feather Books (2003) 3rd Edition.

"Lancashire Dialect" by Peter Wright (1976) – Dalesman Publications Ltd.

"Victorian Yorkshire" by Ian Dewhirst (1972) – Yorkshire Ridings Ltd.

"English Dialects" by M. F. Wakelin (1977) – Athlone Press.

"Discovering English Dialects" by M.F. Wakelin (1978) – Shire Publications.

## RECORDINGS

John Hartley's poems, "Bite Bigger", "Ahr Mary's Bonnet" and "Th'first o'th'sooart" have been recorded by the Yorkshire Dialect Society on their record made at the 1978 Ilkley Literature Festival. Further details of the record may be had from Hon. Librarian, Yorkshire Dialect Society, Spring Hill, Woodside, Edale, Hope Valley, S33 7ZB.

## THE YORKSHIRE DIALECT SOCIETY

More information about the dialect which John Hartley uses can be found in various numbers of the Yorkshire Dialect Society's "Transactions" and in their collections of verse connected with the West Riding. Further details of these publications and of membership, which is open to all those interested in dialect, may be obtained from the

Hon. Treasurer, Mr. Walter Leach, A.C.I.B., 1 Middlewood Close, Kilham, Driffield, North Yorkshire, YO25 4SU or via the website www.ydsociety.org.uk.

John Waddington-Feather was born in 1933 and grew up in a dialect-speaking community in Keighley and Silsden, later graduating at Leeds University where he studied under Professor Harold Orton, who pioneered much dialect study in Britain and North America. Before he retired, John Waddington-Feather was a schoolmaster teaching Standard English, but his plays, novels, short stories, essays and poetry all reflect his deep love for regional English.

He's a Life Member of the Yorkshire Dialect Society, in which he was Hon. Secretary and editor for some years. He was the first chairman of the J.B. Priestley Society and is now a vice-president. In 1985 he was elected a Fellow of the Royal Society of Arts. More information about his writing can be found at his website www.waddysweb.freeuk.com